PLAIN ENGLISH

Book 4

J. Martyn Walsh
Anna Kathleen Walsh

Random House/McCormick-Mathers

International Standard Book Number: 0-800-93014-2

Contents

PAGE

I. Sentence Completeness

Survey Test 1 ... 5
1 Sentence Sense 1 ... 7
2 Sentence Sense 2 ... 8
3 Essential Parts of the Sentence ... 9
4 Predicate Nominative or Appositive ... 10
5 Capitalization and Punctuation ... 11
6 Combining Sentences ... 12
7 Completing Complex Sentences ... 13
8 Combining Sentences ... 14
Spelling List 1 ... 14
9 Completing Sentences ... 15
10 Classifying Sentences and Parts of Speech ... 16

II. Verbs

Survey Test 2 ... 17
11 Classes of Verbs ... 19
12 Classes and Modifications of Verbs ... 20
13 Forming Tenses 1 ... 21
Spelling List 2 ... 21
14 Forming Tenses 2 ... 22
15 Conjugation of the Verb To Give ... 23
16 Forming Tenses 3 ... 24
17 Forming Tenses 4 ... 25
18 Using the Progressive Form of Verbs ... 26
19 Verb Agreement ... 27
Spelling List 3 ... 27
20 Confusing Verbs ... 28
21 Using Verbs 1 ... 29
22 Using Verbs 2 ... 30
23 Using Verbs 3 ... 31
24 Using Verbals ... 32
25 Reviewing Verbs ... 33
Spelling List 4 ... 33
26 Reviewing Verb Agreement ... 34

III. Substantives, Modifiers, and Connectives

Survey Test 3 ... 35
27 Using Nouns ... 37
28 Using Pronouns ... 38
29 Pronoun Agreement ... 39
30 Using Pronouns ... 40
31 Reviewing Pronouns ... 41
32 Reviewing Nouns and Pronouns ... 42
33 Using Adjectives and Adverbs 1 ... 43

PAGE

Spelling List 5 ... 43
34 Using Adjectives and Adverbs 2 ... 44
35 Using Prepositions and Conjunctions ... 45
36 Reviewing Modifiers and Connectives ... 46
37 Reviewing Verbs, Nouns, and Pronouns ... 47
38 Reviewing Verb and Pronoun Agreement ... 48
Spelling List 6 ... 48
39 Reviewing Verbs and Pronouns ... 49
40 Reviewing General Usage ... 50
41 Reviewing Troublesome Usages ... 51
42 Review of Reviews ... 52

IV. Sentence Structure

Survey Test 4 ... 53
43 Phrases and Clauses ... 55
Spelling List 7 ... 55
44 Variety in Sentence Beginnings ... 56
45 Variety in Sentence Structure ... 57
46 Sentence Weaknesses ... 58
47 Sentence Faults ... 59
48 Reviewing Sentence Weaknesses ... 60
49 Capitalization and Punctuation 1 ... 61
50 Capitalization and Punctuation 2 ... 62
51 Using Verbs ... 63
Spelling List 8 ... 63
52 Substantives, Modifiers, Connectives ... 64
53 Reviewing Word Usage ... 65
54 Review of Reviews ... 66

V. Composition and the Use of Words

Survey Test 5 ... 67
55 Paragraph, Précis, and Outline ... 69
56 Letter Writing ... 70
Spelling List 9 ... 70
57 The Business Letter ... 71
58 The Letter of Inquiry ... 72
59 The Friendly Letter ... 73
60 The Letter of Congratulation ... 74
Spelling List 10 ... 74
61 Faulty Expressions in the Sentence/1 ... 75
62 Faulty Expressions in the Sentence/2 ... 76
63 Punctuation and Capitalization Review ... 77
64 Using Words: General Review 1 ... 78
65 Using Words: General Review 2 ... 79
66 Using Words: General Review 3 ... 80

PAGE

Vocabulary

Vocabulary Study/1	81
Vocabulary Study/2	82
Vocabulary Study/3	83
Vocabulary Study/4	84
Vocabulary Study/5	85
Vocabulary Study/6	86
Vocabulary Study/7	87
Vocabulary Study/8	88
Vocabulary Study/9	89
Vocabulary Study/10	90
Vocabulary Study/11	91
Vocabulary Study/12	92
Vocabulary Study/13	93
Vocabulary Study/14	94
Vocabulary Study/15	95
Vocabulary Study/16	96

PAGE

Vocabulary Study/17	97
Vocabulary Study/18	98
Vocabulary Study/19	99
Vocabulary Study/20	100
Vocabulary Study/21	101
Vocabulary Study/22	102

Inventories

Inventory/1	103
Inventory/2	105
Inventory/3	107
Inventory/4	109
Inventory/5	111
Final Inventory/A	113
Final Inventory/B	117
Final Inventory/C	121
Final Inventory/D	125

Sentence Completeness

This test parallels, in content, Inventory 1, page 103.

I. *Sentence Sense*
   (Lessons 1, 2)

15 Points

On the line preceding each group of words, write **0** if the group is not a complete sentence; write **1** if the group is one complete sentence; or write **2** if the group is two sentences incorrectly written as one.

EXAMPLE: _2_ I am going to meet Alicia would you like to go with me?

—— 1 Pat has good ideas she will surely be a good president.

—— 2 Saw Bud and Sue at the show's last performance last night.

—— 3 Ask for a receipt when you pay your dues.

—— 4 While Betty and Danny were shopping.

—— 5 It is a perfect day for the game and everyone is excited.

—— 6 Kay is not here now she is the new chairperson of the committee.

—— 7 Phil and Juan sold all their tickets and collected the money for them.

—— 8 When the day finally arrived for their boat trip.

—— 9 Studying music is interesting have you ever played the piano?

——10 Skiing down the steep mountains in a blinding snowstorm.

——11 It was a very funny comedy you shouldn't have missed it.

——12 We cleaned up the living room after the other guests had gone home.

——13 Marge was here this afternoon I am sorry you couldn't come.

——14 Snow-capped peaks gleaming in the summer sunlight.

——15 Driving through the mountains, we saw a herd of buffalo.

II. *Essential Parts of a Sentence*
   (Lesson 3)

20 Points

Draw one line under the simple subject and draw two lines under the simple predicate of each sentence.

EXAMPLE: Did Jan go to Maine last summer?

1 Did the Sioux Indians live in New England at any time?

2 Around the corner came a large, fast, white camper.

3 Laughing noisily at their games, the children did not hear us.

4 Did you see Starr Walton, the famous skier, at the last party?

5

5 Just beyond that hill is a small lake used as a bird sanctuary.

6 After the cold and gloom of winter comes spring.

7 Has Julie been writing the history of her family?

8 Have you seen any of Shakespeare's plays presented on television?

9 Hoping for a scholarship, Robin has been working at home constantly.

10 Have the plans for your committee meeting been completed?

III. *Combining Groups of Words*
   (Lessons 5–10)

65 Points

Make one complete sentence of the two groups of words in each item by changing punctuation and capitalization. On the line preceding the sentence you reconstruct, give its class by writing **S** for simple, **Cd** for compound, or **Cx** for complex. Above each italicized word, give its part of speech. Use abbreviations.

EXAMPLE:
$$\underline{\text{Cx}}$$
Jim and I *cleaned* the garage/~~After~~ you went home. (with *v* above *cleaned* and *after* above *After*)

_____ 1 Stan Blake is the *captain* of the team. He is a quarterback.

_____ 2 Although she was *greatly* handicapped. She has become a famous athlete.

_____ 3 Zooming across the *cloudless* sky. The jets made a startling noise.

_____ 4 You *surely* will have to work hard. If *you* expect to finish your costume by tonight.

_____ 5 Eugene is intensely interested *in* music. He would like to become a pianist.

_____ 6 Ann is an extremely fast runner. Consequently, she *is* a *valuable* sprinter.

_____ 7 Tracy's stories are *always* interesting. Someday he may be a *fine* novelist.

_____ 8 Lucy will not win the prize. She is *careless* with all her work.

_____ 9 William Saroyan *wrote* "The Parsley Garden." It is a story about a teen-aged boy.

_____10 Helen delivers papers every morning. Yet not once has *she* made poor grades.

_____11 Nell *and* I mowed the lawn. Our other neighbors and Bill played stickball.

_____12 If you cannot get a *plane* reservation. You may have to go by train or bus.

_____13 *Jan* went to a dance last night. It *was* the first time she had been to one.

_____14 If you don't know Lee's telephone number. You *will find* it in the directory.

_____15 Helen Grayson is *unusually* clever. However, she is very careless in her *speech*.

_____16 Fred worked day after day. Hoping to win *the* scholarship.

_____17 Georgia likes all kinds of stories. Especially stories of *adventure*.

_____18 If *you* hope to win the tournament. You are going to have to practice more.

_____19 When you see your *sister*. Please give her this message.

_____20 After the game ended in defeat *for* us. We dropped our plans for a celebration.

SCORE _____ **(Top Score 100)**

Sentence Sense/1

On the line preceding each group of words, write **o** if the group is not a complete sentence; write **1** if the group is one complete sentence; or write **2** if the group is two sentences incorrectly written as one.

EXAMPLE: _2_ Old Silas loved the gold dearly he had nothing else in the world to love.

—— 1 Regarding the child as his own.

—— 2 The old man wished Eppie to be happy.

—— 3 He had been unjustly accused of stealing.

—— 4 He felt that Eppie was a gift from heaven.

—— 5 Telling Silas that she would like a garden.

—— 6 The lonely old man wished to keep the child.

—— 7 Silas Marner in disgrace leaving Lantern Yard.

—— 8 Put yourself in the lonely old weaver's place.

—— 9 Nancy always insisting that Eppie do her duty.

——10 Try to realize just what the loss meant to Silas.

——11 Soon Eppie changed the life of the lonely old man.

——12 Aaron Winthrop was much like his mother he liked to help others.

——13 Eppie growing up to be a favorite in the small community.

——14 Dolly Winthrop and Aaron also called to see Silas.

——15 The money had meant everything to him it was all that he had.

——16 Godfrey Cass, fearing to admit that the child was his.

——17 The old man soon ceased to love gold he was no longer a miser.

——18 Godfrey Cass was indeed a selfish creature he deserved to be childless.

——19 Always eager to do something to make other people happy.

——20 The old man regained much of the faith that he had lost.

——21 Going immediately to the Rainbow and accusing Jem Rodney.

——22 We admire her for refusing to go with Godfrey she really belonged to Silas.

——23 Godfrey and Nancy selfishly hoping to win Eppie away from Silas.

——24 She looked upon Silas as her father no one else could take his place.

——25 Eppie was considerate of her father she surely was a good daughter.

Plain English Handbook, 1–4, 34–37.

Activity: The beginning of the school year is a very good time to practice making introductions. This is a good opportunity to become acquainted with the classmates you do not yet know. Practice introducing your teacher to your classmates and introducing classmates to one another. *Plain English Handbook,* 642 (16).

7

SCORE ——————— (Top Score 25)

Sentence Sense/2

On the line preceding each group of words, write **o** if the group is not a complete sentence; write **1** if the group is one complete sentence; write **2** if the group is two sentences incorrectly written as one; or write **3** if the group is three sentences incorrectly written as one.

EXAMPLE: ___2___ Flags flutter from the stadium a runner carries a torch into the arena.

___ 1 Every four years, amateur athletes from many nations compete in the Olympic Games.

___ 2 The purpose of the Olympic Games to let the great amateur athletes compete.

___ 3 The Summer Olympics run for about two weeks the Winter Olympics last ten days.

___ 4 Relying on individual citizens to pay their Olympic expenses.

___ 5 No other sport spectacle has a background so historic, dramatic, or thrilling.

___ 6 Behind their flags the athletes march into the stadium they stand at attention.

___ 7 A runner carries a blazing torch to announce the opening of the Olympic Games.

___ 8 The trumpets play pigeons are released from their cages the Olympic Games are open.

___ 9 The Summer Games include track events each sport must be carried by 20 countries.

___10 In the bob-sledding events, two- or four-member teams.

___11 Nations do not actually compete against each other no nation officially wins.

___12 Skiing is a Winter Game figure skating is a popular event there are races, also.

___13 In the ancient Olympics, sacrifices of grain, wine, and lambs.

___14 The early games included competition in art forms as well as in athletics.

___15 Criers announcing the winners' names throughout the land.

___16 Women were excluded from the ancient Games as competitors and spectators.

___17 If practiced in accordance with the ancient Greek ideals.

___18 The exact date of the first games is unknown the first recorded race was in 776 B.C.

___19 The first races were in Elis, Greece the races honored Zeus Zeus was a Greek god.

___20 The ancient games were abolished in 392 A.D. the modern games were begun in 1896.

Plain English Handbook, 1–4, 34–37.

Activity: On a separate sheet of paper, make complete sentences of the incomplete sentences above. You will find information about the Olympic Games in your encyclopedia.

SCORE_____(Top Score 20)

Essential Parts of the Sentence

Draw one line under the simple subject and draw two lines under the simple predicate of each sentence.

EXAMPLE: Amelia Earhart flew across the Atlantic Ocean by herself in 1932.

1 The airplane is the most amazing invention of the modern world.

2 People have been thinking of flying for hundreds of years.

3 Leonardo da Vinci drew the earliest known design for a helicopter about 1500.

4 Sir George Cayley frequently is called "the father of the airplane."

5 Otto Lilienthal's gliding research in 1895 led to the invention of the airplane.

6 The first successful fliers were the Wright brothers.

7 Orville Wright's first flight was just 120 feet.

8 Today there are jets that can make nonstop flights of 12,500 miles without refueling.

9 The first planes were largely built of canvas, bamboo, and steel wire.

10 During the early 1900's, daring pilots broke aviation records almost every week.

11 **Baroness Raymonde de Laroche of France became the first licensed woman pilot in 1910.**

12 The first airplane race in the United States was held in 1910.

13 The first round-the-world flight, in 1924, took 175 days.

14 Charles Lindbergh made the first nonstop transatlantic solo flight in 1927.

15 In 1957 three jet bombers flew around the world in 45 hours.

16 Aviation has created new growth patterns for many cities of the world.

17 In some areas of the world rice is now sown from airplanes.

18 Airplanes are also used for crop dusting as well as for air freight.

19 Many private persons now pilot their own airplanes.

20 A well-known poem about flying is "Darius Green and His Flying Machine."

Plain English Handbook, 3, 4, 13, 15.

Activity: On the lines at the bottom of the page, write a paragraph of at least five sentences. Draw one line under each simple subject and draw two lines under each simple predicate.

_____

_____

_____

_____

_____

SCORE _____ (Top Score 40)

9

Predicate Nominative or Appositive

Draw one line under each appositive and draw two lines under each predicate nominative.

EXAMPLE: Casca, the first <u>man</u> to strike Caesar, was a decided <u>radical</u>.

1 Calpurnia was Caesar's wife.

2 Brutus surely was not a great leader.

3 This story of Roman life, as told in *Julius Caesar*, is a grim tragedy.

4 Portia, the wife of Brutus, was Cato's daughter.

5 Titinius, a good friend of Cassius, killed himself.

6 Do you think that Marc Antony, Caesar's grand-nephew, was an effective speaker?

7 Cassius, the leading conspirator, envied all great men.

8 Cassius and Brutus were poor commanders of an army.

9 An interesting character is Lucius, the sleepy musician.

10 Flavius, the tribune, was not a friend of Julius Caesar.

11 Ligarius, the "sick" man, became an ardent conspirator.

12 Cinna, the wily conspirator, was not Cinna, the able poet.

13 The author of this play is William Shakespeare, the great Elizabethan dramatist.

14 Brutus, a great lover of books, placed honor above all else.

15 Perhaps the greatest weakness of Brutus was poor judgment.

16 Brutus, Caesar's best friend, was startled by Caesar's ghost.

17 Artemidorus, the wise teacher, wrote a warning note to Caesar.

18 Did Antony think that the conspirators were honorable men?

19 Brutus, the impractical idealist, sacrificed Caesar, his good friend.

20 In this play Brutus, the desperate conspirator, was a faithless friend.

Plain English Handbook, 96, 100, 101.

Activity: On the lines below, write a short paragraph in which you use predicate nominatives and words in apposition. Mark them as you did in the lesson above.

_____

_____

_____

_____

_____

SCORE _____ (Top Score 30)

Capitalization and Punctuation

Insert punctuation marks where they are needed. Cross out each incorrect mark and each incorrectly capitalized word and write the correct form above it. The numbers in parentheses refer to the *Plain English Handbook*.

history
EXAMPLE: Hal Sloan, Pat's cousin, is studying ~~History~~ this summer.   (500, 471)

1 Edouard Manet a french artist painted "The boy with a sword."   (500, 468, 478)

2 Fighting ceased in World war I on november 11 1918.   (473, 469, 502)

3 Bill saw capt George H Hall last Summer.   (481, 487, 470)

4 When our principal said "do your best for Webb high School we responded whole-heartedly.   (487, 466, 471, 501, 507)

5 Michiko likes Christina G Rossetti's poem "Goblin market."   (487, 500, 478)

6 On Tuesday May 10 Jackie will be twenty one years old.   (502, 534)

7 Julio Martinez is from the south however he is going to school in the north.   (474, 490)

8 Margaret Freeman a canadian girl in our class is studying Mathematics.   (500, 468, 471)

9 A line of Lewis Carrolls poem is "beware the jabberwock, my son!"   (519, 465, 468)

10 Abraham Lincoln read the following books when he was a child the bible *Robinson Crusoe* and *The Pilgrim's Progress*.   (493, 477, 504)

11 My brother is studying spanish this Winter therefore he keeps very busy.   (471, 470, 490)

12 Is the president a member of the republican party.   (482, 471, 529)

13 When Father and I were in the city we saw major Green and her Sister, Sharon.   (497, 481, 482)

14 Carl Sandburg who wrote "Chicago" and other poems is an american poet.   (499, 468)

15 tall slender graceful pines stand at the entrance to our High School.   (464, 505, 471)

16 Jack and i saw general Clay in Dallas Texas last Winter.   (479, 481, 500, 470)

17 Mr. John a. Meyner asked us if we were Juniors in Hale college?   (480, 471, 486, 529)

18 There are twenty three students who study French and spanish.   (534, 471)

19 Margaret went to Mills College we are told to study english and latin.   (500, 471)

20 Yes I wrote my essay on world war II however my teacher hasn't read it yet.   (498, 473, 490)

SCORE _____ (Top Score 75)

Combining Sentences

On the line provided, combine the two simple sentences in each item to form one simple sentence. You may do this by making either the subject or the predicate compound or by using an appositive. Be sure that your punctuation is correct.

EXAMPLE: Fred is our football captain. He is a leader in all sports.
Fred, a leader in all sports, is our football captain.

1 Kay went to a picnic. Jan went to the picnic, too.

2 Mrs. Wilson is our new principal. She seems to be an excellent speaker.

3 Marjorie Kinnan Rawlings wrote *The Yearling*. It is a story about life in Florida.

4 James Thurber has written many books. He has illustrated them himself.

5 Naomi worked on a ranch last summer. Carlos worked on the same ranch.

6 Mary and Bill are in our class. They are both excellent musicians.

7 Juan Gomez is a sensitive, compassionate poet. He is also a good harmonica player.

8 The boys and girls played games. They also sang folk songs.

9 Jo Grant is a member of our club. She is an outstanding leader.

10 Frank Shaw lives in Boston. Tom Stone lives there, too.

11 Juanita won the scholarship. She is the youngest person in our class.

12 The officers of our class wrote the invitations. Then they mailed them.

13 Beth wants to be an atomic scientist. She is our class president.

14 Janie Day went to Canada. Mac Williams went with her.

15 Tom Smith bought a new car. He is my brother's closest friend.

Plain English Handbook, 17, 18, 101, 500.

SCORE _____ (Top Score 15)

Completing Complex Sentences

There are two simple sentences in each item below. On the line provided, rewrite these two sentences to form one **complex** sentence. Be sure that your punctuation is correct.

EXAMPLE: Jan and Terry swam. John and Dana played golf.
While Jan and Terry swam, John and Dana played golf.

1 Sue studied art many years. She had an exhibit of her work in 1974.

2 Bob is critical. He rarely offers suggestions.

3 Newborn ants are small. They have been poorly nourished.

4 Enrico was late to school. He missed his usual bus.

5 Pat began her novel last summer. She was on vacation.

6 Marcia studies hard. She hopes to win a scholarship.

7 Our football team should do well. They worked very hard in practice.

8 Bill completed the entire outline. Helen wrote the story.

9 I was very hungry. I fixed an enormous club sandwich.

10 Hal raced across the goal line. The crowd went wild with joy.

11 The other girls went to a show. Ruth and I played checkers.

12 Red is his favorite color. I am making him a red plaid shirt.

13 Tom did not accept Milton's invitation. He had other plans.

14 Jane is a perfectionist. Her work is always done well.

15 Gail Gault has a keen sense of humor. She can be serious, too.

Plain English Handbook, 23, 414, 497.

13

SCORE _____ (Top Score 15)

Combining Sentences

There are two simple sentences in each item below. On a separate sheet of paper, combine these two sentences in four ways: (1) as a simple sentence, (2) as a compound sentence with the clauses connected by a conjunction, (3) as a compound sentence with the clauses connected by punctuation, and (4) as a complex sentence. Be sure that your punctuation and capitalization are correct. (Review Lessons 6 and 7.)

EXAMPLE: Henry Burr worked on a farm last summer. He learned much about country life.

(1) Working on a farm last summer, Henry Burr learned much about country life. (2) Henry Burr worked on a farm last summer, and he learned much about country life. (3) Henry Burr worked on a farm last summer; he learned much about country life. (4) While he worked on a farm last summer, Henry Burr learned much about country life.

1 I traveled through New England last summer. I was particularly impressed with Cape Cod.
2 George Bernard Shaw wrote many delightful plays. He is popular with many people.
3 That young artist struggled a long time in poverty. She is now successful.
4 Hal Mason is unusually clever. He will do well at the university.
5 Terry Reeves is very much interested in design. He hopes to be a fashion designer.
6 The climate in those mountains is pleasant in summer. In winter it is extremely cold.
7 Ed found an advertisement for a lifeguard. He hurried to apply for the job.
8 Most of us shun the difficult task. Only through hard work can we achieve great things.
9 Sandra has a smile for everyone. Never does she seem unhappy.
10 Our team is working hard in football. They hope to win the game on Saturday.
11 Tom and I finished all our work in the morning. In the afternoon we played tennis.
12 Jack Bailey is extremely conceited. He is not popular with the other students.
13 The professor is very scholarly. He recently published another book.
14 Lou writes excellent stories. Sometimes she uses dialect to add to the effect.
15 Lila is greatly interested in the study of law. Someday she may be a famous attorney.

Plain English Handbook, 20–23, 390, 410, 414, 415, 455, 490, 497.

Activity: Write a letter to a department store, ordering at least five pieces of merchandise. Read sections 587–603 of *Plain English Handbook* for the requirements and correct form of a business letter. Section 603 makes specific suggestions concerning a letter ordering merchandise.

Spelling List/1

advise	disagreeable	irrigate	visible	possible
assistance	scissors	territory	syllable	reasonably
relieve	unique	ordinarily	responsible	ability
impatient	people	instance	remarkable	difficulty
shrieks	especially	attendance	desirable	hastily
knowledge	valleys	wholly	positive	necessity
behavior	revealed	allowed	capable	mechanical
anxious	debtor	already	advisable	notified

SCORE _____ (Top Score 60)

Completing Sentences

By changing capitalization and punctuation, make a complete sentence — simple, compound, or complex — of each of the following items.

EXAMPLES: Bob saw many well-known people/ *while* ~~While~~ he was in New York.

Expecting to attend the hockey game/ *, we* ~~We~~ had an early dinner.

 1 Janet had many exciting times. While she lived in Chicago.

 2 Longing to become a great scientist. That young man is working very hard.

 3 Jean and I were pleased with the plans the other members offered objections.

 4 Hal likes adventure stories. Particularly stories of the old West.

 5 Ann saw many famous actors. When she was in Hollywood last summer.

 6 Planning to start on our trip early the next morning. We went to bed early.

 7 Beth and I had most of the work done. Before the other people arrived.

 8 Fred surely can't expect to win. Unless he improves his tennis game.

 9 Steve and Manuela have arranged the tables Al and Kim will serve refreshments.

10 Kay Strong has appeared on many television shows. Since she went to New York.

11 Edgar Allan Poe wrote horror stories in prose his poetry was usually sad.

12 Bill is studying the contrabassoon it is a woodwind instrument with a very low sound.

13 The other couples waited at the dock. Until Nancy and I arrived.

14 After the basketball game was ended. We planned a big celebration.

15 Ted struggled year after year. Hoping to become a great writer.

16 When Jill went to college. She decided to major in journalism.

17 Overcoming many obstacles. Booker T. Washington became a leader in education.

18 If you expect to go to Europe in two years. You will have to be more thrifty now.

19 Paul Laurence Dunbar wrote many lyrics he wrote both serious and humorous poems.

20 Since he wrote about black life honestly. His works are important historically.

Plain English Handbook, 20–23, 33–37, 490, 495, 497, 499.

Activity: Select a book from the library and prepare an oral book report to give before the class. *Plain English Handbook,* 645.

SCORE _____ (Top Score 20)

Classifying Sentences and Parts of Speech

On the line preceding each sentence, indicate its class by writing **S** for simple, **Cd** for compound, or **Cx** for complex. Above each italicized word, indicate its part of speech by writing **n** for noun, **pron** for pronoun, **adj** for adjective, **adv** for adverb, **v** for verb, **prep** for preposition, or **conj** for conjunction. Class the conjunctive adverb (320) and pronoun (135) as conjunctions.

                                    n   conj pron
EXAMPLE: ___Cx___ Tom doesn't know *where* *he* lost his canteen.

_____ 1 We six *girls* started on our camping *trip early* Saturday morning.

_____ 2 We *packed* our gear carefully, *but* we still had too much to carry *comfortably*.

_____ 3 There *were* only six girls on the trip, *yet* it seemed liked a *larger* group.

_____ 4 We hiked *through* the *woods while* the others finished unpacking their equipment.

_____ 5 The *park* guide wouldn't allow *us* to walk *over* the old, rotted bridge.

_____ 6 If we *hike* steadily, we can *reach* the next campsite *before* dark.

_____ 7 *This* fire has consumed all *those* logs *that* we brought from the woods.

_____ 8 Jan *and* the *other* girls have gone to look for some good *firewood*.

_____ 9 We put up the tents *very* quickly *after* we had built a *roaring* fire.

_____ 10 There were *four* girls *who* took charge of the cooking *chores*.

_____ 11 *We* had good weather all the *time except* Friday evening.

_____ 12 There are *only* three girls swimming *in* the lake *now*.

_____ 13 *Show* me the *stream* that the *others* have found.

_____ 14 *Linda* and I *caught* fifteen *fish* today.

_____ 15 We *watched* the *curious* bear cub carefully knock over our garbage *pail*.

_____ 16 The mother bear *looked* harmless, *but* we did *not* get close enough to find out!

_____ 17 *This* is the sleeping bag *that* Jean borrowed *from* her parents, who camp often.

_____ 18 Ms. Allen, our leader, *was* very pleased *when* we *identified* some constellations.

_____ 19 We must be sure to put out *this fire before* we leave the park.

_____ 20 Our camping *trip* was a great success, *and* it was very *instructive*.

Plain English Handbook, 20–23, 38–45, 52, 138–140.

Activity: Write a short paragraph that contains ten simple sentences. Rewrite your paragraph combining the simple sentences to form five compound or complex sentences.

SCORE _____ (Top Score 80)

Verbs

This test parallels, in content, Inventory 2, page 105.

I. *Transitive and Intransitive Verbs*
(Lessons 11, 12)

10 Points

Draw one line under each transitive verb and two lines under each intransitive verb. Be sure to underline the entire verb.

EXAMPLE: <u>Has</u> your brother <u>sent</u> the book to you?

1 Why did Sue send the picture to me?

2 Has he invited all the seniors to his party?

3 The ocean looked gray and shimmering in the moon's light.

4 The sophomores have been playing some rough games.

5 He should have helped Dan with the report.

6 The sun shines brightly this morning.

7 Mercedes has been writing letters to her family in Mexico.

8 Did Mike speak well before the meeting yesterday?

9 Has the report been sent to the secretary?

10 They should have been planning the program for next week.

17

II. *Tenses of Verbs*
(Lessons 12–18)

15 Points

In each sentence write the correct tense form of the verb in parentheses.

EXAMPLE: (sing — present perfect)   Lee _____ *has sung* _____ her solo already.

1 (swim — past perfect)   Kay _____ across the river yesterday.

2 (rise — past perfect)   The moon _____ before we started to leave.

3 (do — present perfect)   Dick _____ his part unusually well tonight.

4 (lay — past)   The dog _____ himself down on the old rug.

5 (sit — present perfect)   They _____ there ever since the bell rang.

6 (know — past)   Jean _____ that we would do our part.

7 (lie — past perfect)   The kitten _____ there a long while before we left.

8 (see — past)   Jim _____ Clair at the dance last night.

9 (take — past perfect)   She _____ the book before you came.

10 (run — past)   Jack and I _____ to the pool and jumped in.

11 (lie — past)   The dog _____ in the shade while we were working.

12 (go — past perfect)   Gene _____ before we arrived at the station.

13 (give — past)   Tom _____ Lisa some old coins for her collection.

14 (eat — present perfect)   The little dog _____ the large piece of meat.

15 (come — past)   Louise _____ to school with Nan and me.

III. *Using Verbs*
   (Lessons 19–26)   25 Points

Cross out each incorrect verb and write the correct form above it.

                                     sat

EXAMPLE: Joe and she came in and ~~set~~ at a table near the door.

1 Here comes Mr. Hall and his students.

2 The man had not spoke until he raised to his feet.

3 The class thinks you was the one who done the best work this year.

4 Are you sure it is I who is to make this report?

5 If I was he, I'd do as the others have did.

6 Hank is one of those people who is always eager for fun.

7 Neither Miss Field nor the speakers was here when we come.

8 Was Bob and his sister at the airport when you seen them?

9 Fred don't know whether the other boys have went home or not.

10 The puppy has been laying beside the heater since he come in.

11 We don't know which one of the girls are selling the tickets.

12 Our glee club were invited to sing when they give their last party.

13 A great number of students was here when Dick run in the contest.

14 Before the rain begun to fall, we had done the work she had gave us.

15 After the hard work we had done, bread and butter were good food.

18

SCORE _____ (Top Score 50)

Classes of Verbs

Draw one line under each transitive verb and draw two lines under each intransitive verb. Be sure to underline all parts of the verb.

EXAMPLE: <u>Have</u> all the sophomores <u>bought</u> tickets for the seniors' variety show?

1 Tina surely did well in the contest last night.
2 Did your team defeat ours in the soccer game yesterday?
3 Has the new committee arranged the next program?
4 Jack sang two songs for us at the party last night.
5 When did Alice return from her trip to New Orleans?
6 That cat has been sitting on the fence for an hour or more.
7 The other girls must have brought the props for the stage.
8 Helena is writing interesting stories about her recent trip to Spain.
9 Did Liza and Henry play tennis this morning before school?
10 Shall we play another game of badminton now, or after lunch?

Plain English Handbook, 173–176, 212.

Draw one line under each complete verb and draw two lines under each linking (copulative) verb.

EXAMPLE: We <u>sat</u> beside the old mill for about an hour.

11 There are many excellent students in our school this year.
12 The little girl ran happily around the newly mown field.
13 Many children played among the big trees in the park.
14 We camped for a month in the Green Mountains of Vermont.
15 The old cabin stood on a little hill above the foot trail.
16 In the autumn evening we sat around a cheerful campfire.
17 The Appalachian Mountains in North Carolina look beautiful in their autumn colors.
18 Our principal has gone to a meeting of educators in the East.
19 That is certainly the most unusual car in the automobile show this year.
20 We looked across the great plains toward the high mountains.

Plain English Handbook, 177, 178, 180.

Activity: Write sentences using each of the following verbs, or a form of each of the verbs, as a transitive verb and as an intransitive verb. Then classify each verb as regular or irregular. *Plain English Handbook,* 171. 172, 176.

1 sing	3 drive	5 study	7 turn
2 move	4 help	6 eat	8 meet

SCORE _____ (Top Score 20)

LESSON 12

Classes and Modifications of Verbs

Indicate the class of each italicized verb by writing **t** above it if it is transitive or **i** if it is intransitive. If the verb is transitive, indicate its voice by writing **a** for active or **p** for passive after the **t**. If the verb is intransitive, indicate whether it is complete or linking by writing **c** or **l** after the **i**.

i-l
EXAMPLE: Jack Barry *is* the best swimmer at our local YMCA.

1 I *should have been preparing* my Spanish lesson for tomorrow.

2 That lazy student *might have been* the leader of our class.

3 The horses cantering along the bridle path *were* tired.

4 More than half of the students in our school band *are* juniors.

5 This delightful book *was written* by a little-known American author.

6 We *had* a good time at the picnic in the park yesterday.

7 Our basketball team *has been defeated* only once this season.

8 We *fished* in a little mountain stream near a pine forest.

9 East High's best player *became* angry during the game yesterday.

10 The seniors *are working* on their assembly program for next week.

Plain English Handbook, 173–180, 184, 185, 212.

Indicate the tense of each verb by writing above it **pres** for present, **past** for past, **fut** for future, **pres per** for present perfect, **past per** for past perfect, or **fut per** for future perfect.

pres per
EXAMPLE: The orchestra and band have begun plans for the music festival.

11 Surely the bell rang a long time ago.

12 Joe will run in the mile race next Wednesday.

13 The river has risen several feet within the last hour.

14 They have sat there on that bench for more than an hour.

15 Speak to Ms. Williams about the price of the tickets for the play.

16 She will not have finished her story by this afternoon.

17 Harold and I swam across Round Lake yesterday afternoon.

18 The workers will have laid the last brick by tomorrow night.

19 Don had not written his application letter at noon today.

20 The high school rock band will play for us at the school dance tomorrow evening.

Plain English Handbook, 190–196, 207.

SCORE _____ (Top Score 30)

Forming Tenses/1

In each sentence write the correct form of the verb indicated in the parentheses.

EXAMPLE: (ring — past perfect)   The bell _____*had rung*_____ before I opened the door.

1 (**swim** — past)   The girls _____ to the deep end of the pool.

2 (**see** — past)   Barry _____ the Veterans' parade yesterday.

3 (**lie** — past perfect)   We _____ on the grass to rest awhile.

4 (**do** — past)   Robert _____ his very best to win his race.

5 (**come** — future perfect)   Jack _____ before ten o'clock tonight.

6 (**swing** — past)   My cousin _____ her bat carelessly.

7 (**bring** — past)   Neither boy _____ his own pencil.

8 (**do** — present perfect)   Ann _____ the work for us.

9 (**drink** — present perfect)   They _____ all the milk in the refrigerator.

10 (**blow** — past)   The wind _____ hard all day yesterday.

11 (**know** — future)   She _____ the results of her exam before lunch.

12 (**lie** — past)   The traveler _____ down in the shade of that linden tree.

13 (**eat** — past perfect)   Toni _____ her lunch before we arrived.

14 (**break** — past perfect)   We heard that he _____ the school record.

15 (**ring** — past)   Class had started before the bell _____.

16 (**give** — past)   My brother _____ me this sweater for Christmas.

17 (**throw** — past perfect)   Mrs. Young _____ the small fish back into the lake.

18 (**lie** — present)   That lazy kitten _____ on the couch every day.

19 (**shake** — future perfect)   Jim _____ the smaller rugs before he leaves.

20 (**go** — past perfect)   Catrina _____ when we arrived at her house.

Plain English Handbook, 190–196, 204, 207, 216, 217.

21

Spelling List/2

deceive	inquiry	industrial	awkward	juvenile
precious	partial	acres	experience	strict
science	confer	relatives	lecture	harmony
neither	glimpse	existed	solemn	apogee
neighbors	advertisement	actual	adjust	depot
species	interfere	various	wisdom	university
ancient	luncheon	fission	theme	journal
young	maintenance	sacred	pierced	equipment

SCORE _____ (Top Score 20)

Forming Tenses/2

In each sentence write the correct tense form indicated in the parentheses.

EXAMPLE: (take — present perfect)   The coach _____*has taken*_____ the track team to the meet.

1 (rise — past)   The unhappy defendant _____ to her feet reluctantly.

2 (go — present perfect)   Are you sure the boys _____ to the game?

3 (sink — present perfect)   The sun _____ from sight behind the mountains.

4 (sit — past perfect)   They _____ at the airport for over an hour.

5 (set — past)   Rich very carefully _____ the Chinese vase on the table.

6 (know — past)   Tish _____ the answer, but she was not called upon in class.

7 (rise — future perfect)   The river _____ a foot by this evening.

8 (shake — present perfect)   I'm afraid Tom _____ that tree too hard.

9 (rise — past perfect)   The moon _____ before we sailed the boat to shore.

10 (sit — present)   We often just _____ beside the pool and dangle our feet.

11 (ride — present perfect)   Donna _____ her horse in many shows by now.

12 (sing — past perfect)   The seniors _____ many school songs that we had never heard.

13 (speak — present perfect)   Kate _____ with the principal about the matter.

14 (swim — past perfect)   Jan _____ across the pool twice before I dived in.

15 (write — present perfect)   Sue _____ a magazine article about rock music.

16 (tear — past perfect)   The wind _____ the small sailboat from its moorings.

17 (do — future perfect)   Bill _____ his lessons by the time we are to leave.

18 (grow — present perfect)   Jill _____ three inches since we last saw her.

19 (sink — past perfect)   The *Titanic* _____ before the *Carpathia* could reach her.

20 (throw — past)   Jo _____ her sweater over her shoulder and hurried to the court.

Plain English Handbook, 190–196, 204, 207–209, 216, 217.

Activity: Review carefully the principal parts of the verbs listed in *Plain English Handbook,* 204. If you know the principal parts of a verb, you will be able to form any tense easily. Write the principal parts of each of the verbs given above.

SCORE _____ (Top Score 20)

Conjugation of the Verb *To Give*

On each line write the correct form for the conjugation of the verb *to give* in the active voice, indicative mood.

Present Tense

SINGULAR

1 I _____

2 you _____

3 he _____

PLURAL

1 we _____

2 you _____

3 they _____

Past Tense

1 I _____

2 you _____

3 he _____

1 we _____

2 you _____

3 they _____

Future Tense

1 I _____

2 you _____

3 he _____

1 we _____

2 you _____

3 they _____

Present Perfect Tense

1 I _____

2 you _____

3 he _____

1 we _____

2 you _____

3 they _____

Past Perfect Tense

1 I _____

2 you _____

3 he _____

1 we _____

2 you _____

3 they _____

Future Perfect Tense

1 I _____

2 you _____

3 he _____

1 we _____

2 you _____

3 they _____

Plain English Handbook, 183, 184, 186, 187, 190–196, 204, 205, 207.

Activity: On a separate sheet of paper, write the conjugation of *to give* in the progressive form (209). Write the conjugation of *to give* in the passive voice, indicative mood (185, 208).

SCORE _____ (Top Score 36)

Forming Tenses/3

A verb is given at the beginning of each group of sentences below. In each sentence of the group write the tense form of this verb called for in the parentheses. The **p** following the tense indication means that the form is to be passive; otherwise all forms are to be active.

EXAMPLES: break

(past perfect)   The wind _____*had broken*_____ three windows.

(present perfect — **p**)   Three windows _____*have been broken*_____ by the wind.

give

1 (past)   Are you sure that he _____ you the correct number of tickets?

2 (future)   Larry _____ you your tickets by noon tomorrow.

3 (past — **p**)   The prize _____ to the person who sold the most tickets.

4 (present perfect)   Pat's mother _____ us an order for 30 tickets.

come

5 (future perfect)   They _____ to the meeting by seven.

6 (past)   The boys _____ early to help clean up the clubroom.

7 (present perfect)   Some girls _____ to help us set up the chairs.

lie

8 (present)   Our big black cat often _____ on that window seat.

9 (past perfect)   One day we found that he _____ on the mantel all night.

10 (past)   We _____ on the lawn and watched him try to catch a blowing leaf.

11 (present perfect)   That lazy cat _____ there and watched us all day.

raise

12 (past)   The chairperson quickly _____ the question himself.

13 (past perfect — **p**)   A discussion _____ about the last motion.

rise

14 (past perfect)   Ken _____ from treasurer to chairperson in a short time.

15 (past)   The students _____ to their feet when the president entered.

16 (present perfect)   The chairperson _____ to introduce the speaker.

sit

17 (present)   That old man _____ near me in my pottery class.

18 (past perfect)   He _____ there often before we ever noticed him.

19 (past)   We _____ in the boat while Jim rowed it around the pond.

20 (present perfect — **p**)   The bench _____ on by many different people.

Plain English Handbook, 184, 185, 190–196, 204, 207, 208, 216, 217.

Activity: Write the principal parts of each of the six verbs used in this lesson. *Plain English Handbook*, 204.

SCORE _____ (Top Score 20)

Forming Tenses/4

A verb is given at the beginning of each group of sentences below. In each sentence of the group write the tense form of this verb called for in the parentheses. The **p** following the tense indication means that the form is to be passive; otherwise all forms are to be active.

EXAMPLES: **lay**

(past) Sam _____ *laid* _____ the silverware on the table.

(present perfect — **p**) Many stones _____ *have been laid* _____ for a rock garden.

speak

1 (past perfect) I wish you _____ with me about this matter.

2 (past — **p**) The words _____ very distinctly by the radio announcer.

3 (present perfect) That man certainly _____ plainly enough.

swim

4 (future perfect) She _____ across the pool four times without a rest.

5 (present perfect) All the campers _____ across the lake already.

6 (past) Susan and I _____ until we were **exhausted.**

7 (past perfect) Bob _____ in many other contests before this one.

sing

8 (present perfect — **p**) That old song _____ many times.

9 (past perfect) James _____ his solo before you came into the room.

10 (past — **p**) The big soprano part _____ by Helen Erickson.

see

11 (future perfect) He _____ the principal before he sees us.

12 (past) Barbara and I _____ the Mayan art exhibit yesterday.

13 (past perfect — **p**) The stranger _____ by several of the boys.

go

14 (present perfect) All the students _____ to today's game.

15 (future perfect) Freda _____ before our plane arrives.

16 (past perfect) I wish I _____ to the horse show with the others.

do

17 (past) Betty _____ excellent work in school last year.

18 (present perfect) The girls _____ their jobs very quickly.

19 (past perfect) I wish we _____ our work before the party.

20 (present perfect — **p**) Most of the planning _____ by Louise.

Plain English Handbook, 174, 175, 190–196, 204, 207, 208, 216.

Activity: In original sentences use the verbs given above in all six tenses.

25

SCORE _____ (Top Score 20)

LESSON 18

Using the Progressive Form of Verbs

In each sentence write the correct progressive tense form indicated in the parentheses.

EXAMPLE: (blow — present perfect) The storm _____*has been blowing*_____ violently for an hour.

1 (swim — future) If we hurry we _____ in the lake soon.

2 (rise — past) The moon _____ over the hills as we left the party.

3 (go — present) The students _____ to their classes now.

4 (do — present perfect) Anita _____ her work well this term.

5 (see — future) We _____ Carol and Chuck very soon.

6 (sing — past) The glee club _____ with only piano accompaniment.

7 (ring — past) The bell for class _____ when I left home.

8 (lie — past) Your coat _____ on the chair when I last saw it.

9 (ride — present) Tony _____ his new motor scooter today.

10 (set — present) Mary _____ a good example for the others.

11 (raise — past perfect) Tom _____ the windows for Mrs. James.

12 (drive — future) Rita _____ her new sports coupe to the lake.

13 (write — present perfect) Ellen _____ her theme for tomorrow.

14 (give — past) The chairperson _____ his report when they entered.

15 (lie — present perfect) That book _____ on the floor all day.

16 (come — past perfect) Until last week Joe _____ to school early.

17 (lay — present) The workers _____ the foundation for the new school.

18 (lay — past perfect) The mason _____ the bricks for our fireplace.

19 (sit — future) They _____ there, just as they are now, when we return.

20 (speak — past perfect) Ruth _____ to the class when we came into the room.

Plain English Handbook, 190–196, 204, 207–212, 216, 217.

Activity: Write a note inviting a friend to a picnic that you are giving next weekend. Be sure to include all the necessary information. *Plain English Handbook*, 617.

SCORE _____ (Top Score 20)

26

Verb Agreement

In each sentence write the correct verb form from within the parentheses.

EXAMPLE: (is/are) Every one of the Coopers _____is_____ blond.

1 (am/is) It is I who _____ to blame for the unfortunate error.

2 (is/are) Ham and eggs _____ a favorite American dish.

3 (was/were) Our glee club _____ very popular this year.

4 (is/are) One of our exchange students _____ from Mexico.

5 (are/is) A large and a small boat _____ on the lake now.

6 (Are/Is) _____ Bob and his cousin going skating with us?

7 (is/are) Neither Joan nor Miss Dale _____ here right now.

8 (was/were) The director, not the players, _____ responsible.

9 (were/was) Sixty dollars _____ paid for the new art room equipment.

10 (was/were) Neither the coach nor the players _____ in the locker room.

11 (don't/doesn't) The teacher _____ permit the class to get noisy.

12 (come/comes) Here _____ the members from the Honor Society meeting.

13 (is/are) The number of sophomores _____ unusually large this year.

14 (was/were) Each of the girls _____ doing her best to win the game.

15 (was/were) The director, as well as the actors, _____ grateful for his praise.

16 (is/are) Each of the students _____ selling tickets for Saturday's dance.

17 (are/is) A great number of students _____ planning to go on to college.

18 (is/are) Dotty is one of those persons who _____ always pleasant.

19 (is/are) It is one of those decisions that _____ always difficult to make.

20 (was/were) Plenty of meat _____ provided for the school barbecue by a local rancher.

Plain English Handbook, 197, 236–242, 244, 246, 261.

Activity: The merchandise which you ordered in Lesson 8 has been delivered to you, but one article is defective. Write to the department store, carefully explaining the unsatisfactory condition of the article. Be sure to plan your letter before you write it. *Plain English Handbook*, 610.

27

Spelling List/3

happier	concession	response	literature	fusion
accomplish	spacecraft	particularly	distribute	toboggans
experiments	rebellion	investigate	benefited	handful
usually	manual	lift-off	description	advertising
issue	introduction	volume	witness	interview
accompany	expressing	expensive	occasion	vacancy
referred	scarcity	brilliant	demonstration	postpone
opportunity	endurance	superintendent	discuss	religious

SCORE _____ (Top Score 20)

Confusing Verbs

In each sentence write the correct forms of the verbs given.

EXAMPLE: rise, raise

The cost of living must _____rise_____ before sellers can _____raise_____ prices for their merchandise.

sit, set

1 We must have _____ out at least twenty plants before we _____ down to rest.

2 Mom _____ in her favorite chair, and _____ her book and glasses on the end table beside her.

3 We _____ down at the table, and the waiter _____ a menu in front of each of us.

4 Mother _____ the turkey on the table while we _____ and admired it.

5 Don and Jack have _____ there ever since we _____ that bench in the shade.

6 Ray _____ a bowl of meat before the dog, but the dog just _____ and looked at it.

7 After we had _____ the hurdles in place, we _____ on the bench with Tom.

lie, lay

8 Your coat is still _____ on the same chair where you _____ it.

9 The banner is _____ on the ground, but I did not _____ it there.

10 The dog will _____ down close to where his master is now _____.

11 While I was _____ on the beach, a black cocker spaniel came and _____ beside me.

12 Where did you _____ the book? It must still be _____ there.

13 We'll let the new carpet _____ here until someone can _____ it for us.

14 The money has _____ on the mantelpiece since you _____ it there last week.

rise, raise

15 We should have _____ when the judge _____ from the bench.

16 Tom had already _____ to speak before Don _____ a new objection.

17 If you _____ the oven heat now, your cake will not _____ well.

18 You may _____ the window if the wind has not _____.

19 The temperature was _____ rapidly when we _____ to start on our hike.

20 The speaker _____ his hand, and the audience _____ to its feet.

Plain English Handbook, 190–196, 204, 207–212, 217.

SCORE _____ (Top Score 40)

Using Verbs/1

Cross out each incorrect verb and write the correct form above it. If there is no incorrect verb, write **C** before the sentence.

EXAMPLE: They had ~~went~~ *gone* only a short way when they had a flat tire.   (204)

1 Are you sure that it is I who is to blame?   (249)

2 Can Helen and I borrow your record player, Pedro?   (218)

3 Jaime went home and done his homework.   (204, 216)

4 Were you at the game when Tom seen you?   (260, 204, 216)

5 Each of the players were making every effort to win.   (242)

6 We found that five miles were too long a distance to walk.   (245)

7 I could of sat there an hour listening to his talk.   (230, 217)

8 It is one of those subjects that is always interesting.   (241)

9 If she offers me the job, I promise I will except it.   (220, 228)

10 Was you appointed chairperson of the art committee?   (260, 185)

11 Gwen says that she has already did her assigned book report.   (204, 216)

12 My little brother growed about three inches last year.   (204)

13 The coach has done his best to learn James to throw good passes.   (216, 227)

14 Did anyone in Biblical times believe that the earth was round?   (251)

15 Neither the book nor the pencils is lying on the table now.   (238, 217)

16 There was four students nominated for the presidency of the club.   (239)

17 We should raise to our feet when Judge Trowbridge comes in.   (204, 216, 217)

18 The coach, no less than the players, is to blame for what they did.   (236, 216)

19 The bracelet that Terry give me should be lying on the table.   (204, 216, 217)

20 We came early, but you had already went to the skating rink.   (203, 216)

21 If I was only a little older, Mother would teach me to drive our car.   (256, 227)

22 Have you seen the book I lay on the desk a few minutes ago?   (204, 216, 217)

23 We had set there for fifteen minutes before the play began.   (204, 217)

24 A great number of trees was broken in the hurricane last summer.   (244, 185, 204)

25 I am sure that one of the girls have taken the tickets that Al gave us.   (246, 185, 204)

Numbers in parentheses refer to *Plain English Handbook.*

29

SCORE _____ (Top Score 25)

Using Verbs/2

Cross out each incorrect verb and write the correct form above it. If there is no incorrect verb, write **C** before the sentence.

EXAMPLE: There ~~was~~ *were* seven passengers waiting at the bus stop when I arrived.

1 Bob had not wrote his paper when I saw him this morning.

2 One of the new players are here, but the coach has already gone home.

3 We drunk the lemonade before we started our tennis match.

4 Hank brung the tickets to the hockey game to us yesterday.

5 I begun typing my story on conservation right after breakfast.

6 The starting bell has rung, but Jack has not came to class yet.

7 If the book is tore, we should report it to the librarian.

8 All the girls done their best, but they were defeated.

9 This catcher's mitt was almost wore out when Hal gave it to me.

10 As soon as Tim had eaten his breakfast, he run to catch the school bus.

11 The doorbell had rang some five times before anyone heard it.

12 There was two children with Larry when we saw him at the new art museum.

13 All the girls have ate lunch, and some of them have already gone to class.

14 Paul don't like that subject, though he has done excellent work in it.

15 If they had began serious practice earlier, they would have done better.

16 After we had driven a short way, we seen that we had taken the wrong turning.

17 The boys have finished their sandwiches, but they have not eaten dessert.

18 The boys have done the decorating of the gym, and most of them have went home.

19 Charles give me this book before he hurried off to his English class.

20 The track team has done very well, but it has not broke any records.

Plain English Handbook, 190–197, 204, 207–208, 216, 239, 246.

Activity: Pronunciation must be correct if we are to be understood. Section 675 in *Plain English Handbook* lists words which are frequently mispronounced. Using a dictionary, study the marking of each of these words until you can pronounce each correctly. The section on pronunciation, pages 11a to 24a, at the front of *Webster's Intermediate Dictionary* gives complete information on the subject.

SCORE _____ (Top Score 20)

Using Verbs/3

To complete each of the following sentences insert the correct form of the verb within the parentheses.

EXAMPLE: Neither Jill nor I _____*was*_____ (were/was) at the airport when he arrived.

1 More than two-thirds of the students _____ (were/was) at the meeting.

2 Lorrie flies in jet planes often, but she has not _____ (flew/flown) in a helicopter.

3 Most of the civilian airliners flying now _____ (are/is) jets and, there _____ (are/is) now in service the giant 747's.

4 Each of the jets _____ (are/is) powered by kerosenelike fuel.

5 When the storm _____ (come/came) close, he _____ (ran/run) down to the cellar.

6 Either Miss Fields or one of the administrators _____ (are/is) to go to the meeting.

7 Tim and I _____ (seen/saw) Jan during halftime at the football game.

8 When I saw Pete yesterday, he _____ (give/gave) me this message for you.

9 We had _____ (went/gone) to the play before Dave came with the tickets.

10 Jim had never been in an airplane, yet he _____ (begun/began) to write about one.

11 Ms. James poured a glass of water and the small boy _____ (drunk/drank) it thirstily.

12 Plenty of activities _____ (were/was) planned for the class exhibit.

13 The first U. S. civilian jet liner was _____ (flew/flown) from New York to Paris.

14 Emilia is one of those girls who _____ (are/is) always very assertive.

15 Neither the coach nor the player _____ (are/is) to be blamed for the error.

16 The record for the high jump was _____ (broke/broken) by someone from our school.

17 _____ (Are/Is) the committee ready to hand in their votes?

18 One of the principal members of the cast _____ (was/were) sick on opening night.

Plain English Handbook, 197, 204, 207, 208, 216, 237–244, 246.

Activity: Choose a topic and write a short theme. The topic may be developed by means of details, examples, comparison or contrast, cause and effect, or a combination of any two or more of these methods. *Plain English Handbook,* 544–545.

SCORE _____ (Top Score 20)

LESSON 24

Using Verbals

In each sentence write the correct expression from within the parentheses.

EXAMPLE: (Tom/Tom's) We were proud of _____Tom's_____ winning the high dive.

1 (having started/starting)   Janet has been working a month, _____ the first of May.

2 (me/I)   Harry took him to be _____.

3 (she/her)   Joe thought me to be _____.

4 (I/me)   Luisa was thought to be _____.

5 (he/him)   You were thought to be _____.

6 (he/him)   Were you believed to be _____?

7 (Who/Whom)   _____ did you take me to be?

8 (him/his)   We encouraged _____ entering the next contest.

9 (you/your)   I am delighted at _____ learning to sail your new boat.

10 (she/her)   The teacher must have taken me to be _____.

11 (to work/working)   To play is as important as _____.

12 (me/my)   He was disappointed at _____ losing the last race.

13 (us/our)   Did the janitor report _____ writing on the walls?

14 (Kim/Kim's)   Are you in favor of _____ representing the class tomorrow?

15 (them/their)   The explorer told us about _____ discovering Crystal Cave.

16 (you/your)   I think that _____ coming with us is a very good idea.

17 (playing/to play)   I think playing tennis is better exercise than _____ golf.

18 (departing/having departed)   She has been gone a month, _____ on June 20.

19 (money was saved/we saved money)   By taking the bus, _____.

20 (having met/meeting)   Jane and I are no longer strangers, _____ one another last week.

Plain English Handbook, 198–201, 264, 270, 274, 450.

Activity: Making a speech gives excellent practice in using good English and in securing poise and confidence before a group. During the school year numerous occasions offer opportunities for speech activities. During fire prevention week, at Christmas time or at Thanksgiving, or during a charity drive, occasions arise which call for speeches. Write a speech urging your classmates to support some worthy cause or expressing the true spirit of a holiday. *Plain English Handbook*, 643.

SCORE _____ (Top Score 20)

LESSON 25

Reviewing Verbs

Cross out each incorrect verb and write its correct form above it.

EXAMPLE: When Barbara and I looked at our basement, we ~~seen~~ *saw* a fine place for a recreation room.

1 Last week, Barbara and I drawed plans for a basement recreation room.

2 Mom and Dad hoped they had did the right thing by letting us decorate it ourselves.

3 Before we begun painting the room, we measured the walls and floor.

4 We knowed exactly how much paint we would need before we started.

5 Images of an architect's dream growed in our minds as we painted.

6 After we had ate lunch, we hurried back to the basement.

7 Reb, our dog, had broke our only lamp.

8 Some of his fur had sticked on the newly painted walls.

9 We thought we could cover it with some posters Cousin Arlene had give us.

10 To make matters worse, our little brother had rode through on his tricycle; we now have a striped floor!

11 I should have took them both outside and locked the doors before we started.

12 On the next day we give most of our attention to bookshelves.

13 Mom had drove us to the lumberyard to get wood for the shelves.

14 We started to make the bookshelves, but we drived the nails in incorrectly.

15 I wondered if Barbara ever regretted that she had chose to begin this project.

16 After several hours of sawing and hammering, I certainly begun to wonder why we had ever wanted a rec room!

17 The do-it-yourself bookshelves we seen in a magazine seemed so easy to do.

18 We could have sang for joy when we had to stop for dinner.

19 Dad said he should have did some carpentry work with us to give us practice using tools.

20 Maybe we should have chose an easier project.

Plain English Handbook, 190–196, 204, 216.

Spelling List/4

annual	desirous	guitars	capsule	belief
possession	pamphlet	accurate	tournament	assume
institute	urgent	elevator	crisis	whistle
electricity	initiation	ridiculous	portion	affect
aviation	element	arctic	sought	temperamental
variety	unfortunate	omitted	expression	altitude
explanation	access	establish	interruption	agriculture
insurance	preparations	schedule	title	sacrifice

SCORE _____ (Top Score 20)

Reviewing Verb Agreement

Cross out each incorrect verb and write the correct form above it. If there is no incorrect verb, write **C** before the sentence.

EXAMPLE: There ~~was~~ *were* twelve girls in the group, but only four were sophomores.   (239)

1 If I was king, I would declare every Monday a holiday. (256)

2 It seems that Bob don't know which of the girls is leader.   (197, 246)

3 Doesn't the hat and jacket lying on that chair belong to Rolando?   (197)

4 A large number of students is going to the table tennis match today.   (244)

5 We thought that twenty dollars were too much for that old chair.   (245)

6 The number of traffic accidents over Memorial Day was very large.   (244)

7 One of the boys are here, but neither of the girls has come yet.   (246, 242)

8 If Jill were at the meeting, neither she nor Don has said so.   (257, 237)

9 Helen is one of those people who is always very competitive.   (197, 241)

10 There were few ancients who believed that the earth was round.   (239, 251)

11 Everyone of the girls now talks as if she was acting a part in a play.   (242, 258)

12 Jenny, as well as Sue, were here; but there were others to come.   (236, 239)

13 A black and a blue car was parked in front of Jim's house yesterday.   (248)

14 If I was you, I'd ask one of those clerks who are always so pleasant.   (256, 241)

15 You was the first winner, but neither of the others has been chosen.   (260, 242)

16 There is two volunteers to work at the booth, but one of them is not here.   (239, 246)

17 Each of the columnists think that our team is sure to win the soccer trophy.   (242, 240)

18 There are many good desserts, but peaches and cream are my favorite.   (239, 247)

19 Neither Kay nor Dan have joined the club, but Jean and Lou are members.   (237, 247)

20 Neither the typists nor the secretary have been here since you were elected chairperson.   (238, 260)

21 Neither Ed nor the newcomers has sent the money to the treasurer.   (237, 247)

22 The actors, not the director, thinks the drama club is ready for the play. (261, 240)

23 The jury have made a decision, and everyone is eager to hear the verdict. (240, 242)

24 Kay doesn't know that a number of her friends has been invited to the party. (197, 244)

25 Neither Hank nor Nina thinks that two hundred dollars is too much for that old car. (237, 245)

Substantives, Modifiers, and Connectives

This test parallels, in content, Inventory 3, page 107.

I. *Using Substantives*
  (Lessons 27–32, 37–42)   30 Points

Cross out each incorrect noun or pronoun and write the correct form above it.

EXAMPLE: Joan and he have brought a picnic lunch for ~~we~~ *us* club members.

1 Joe and I have two sister-in-laws now.

2 Is it he whom you think is taller than I?

3 Who did he say sent Hal and I the tickets?

4 Jackie and she are much younger than Bob and him.

5 All we boys but George and he will go to the county fair.

6 How can I find Dr. Lane's and Dr. Sullivan's office?

7 I am quite sure it was him who came with Dorothy and her.

8 Margarita and I used two cupsful of sugar in the cake.

9 All us students think it was he whom we saw with her.

10 Could it have been her whom you saw with Jack and him?

11 Was it him who made the plans for the meeting of us boys?

12 It must have been them who brought these books for Jim and me.

13 Was it Gayle and she who took Paul and he to their club dance?

14 James and her are the two who are to go with Suzanne and me.

15 Aunt Grace gave Louise and I enough chairs for all of us cousins and our guests.

16 The jacket hanging on that hook looks like my brother's-in-law.

17 Was it she and Luis whom we saw at the theater with Vic and she?

18 Was it he whom you asked to bring the costumes down to we actors?

19 Are Miss Martinez and she going with we girls to the newspaper office?

20 Every girl on the crew will do their best to help us win the race.

21 Could it have been them who sent us the newspaper clippings?

22 Whomever is elected will take office next September.

23 This is somebody's else book, because I am sure that it is not mine.

24 Hugo and she have made sketches of all of us students except Dot and she.

35

25 All us students should encourage our team to maintain its reputation.

26 Hank works in the boy's shop at Jordan's, and Judy is in the hardware department.

27 He is a newspaper columnist whom we think is a friend to all us students.

28 Each girl in the class should take their problems to the counselor, Ms. Williams.

29 Bill and I think that Bess and her will help us players get the tennis courts in order.

30 Jan thinks that mooses are the most ungainly and homely animals in the United States.

II. *Using Modifiers and Connectives*
   (Lessons 33–36, 40–42)   20 Points

Cross out each incorrect adjective, adverb, preposition, or conjunction and write the correct form above it.

beautiful
EXAMPLE: The mountains looked ~~beautifully~~ in the early morning sunlight.

1 The pineapple looked good, but it tasted bitterly.

2 The team cannot win except it practices regularly.

3 Tom has a small build, but he plays football good.

4 Ann feels badly because she spoke so rudely yesterday.

5 There is not no reason for her treating us so indifferently.

6 Roberto feels some better today, but he still feels bad.

7 Jack played very well, but he was not no match for Bill.

8 We catchers surely make less mistakes on the baseball field now.

9 Although he is the youngest of the three, he sure plays well.

10 When we came into the room, Ken was sitting in back of the desk.

11 We could have done this more quickly if we had done it different.

12 Although Cathy is not nearly so large as Mona, she is the best athlete.

13 Jean is somewhat upset because she cannot find her jacket anywheres.

14 The stories are real interesting, but they are not carefully written.

15 I read in the paper where the weather is to be somewhat colder today.

16 Nan was the tallest of my two cousins who went skating with Beth and me.

17 Your pen is different than Bob's or mine, but it is the best of the three.

18 Maria, the older of the two sisters, hopes to finish the course inside of two years.

19 Although Ed and I are twins, we differ with each other in looks and personality.

20 This car is different than the others, for the steering wheel is on the right side.

SCORE _____ (Top Score 50)

Using Nouns

Cross out each noun used incorrectly and write the correct form above it. If there is no incorrect noun, write **C** before the sentence.

lives
EXAMPLE: Many ~~lifes~~ have been saved by the discovery of penicillin.   (82)

  1 Are oxes still used as farm animals in India?   (85)

  2 The farmers in the valleys grow many potatoes each year.   (81, 78)

  3 Weren't you surprised at Kay's refusing the part of Juliet?   (127)

  4 We brought back two deers from our hunting trip in Wisconsin.   (89)

  5 It is very important that all jockies remain light in weight.   (81)

  6 Jan and Al's hands were dirty after they had changed the tire.   (125)

  7 Fred is going to take his father's-in-law new car to the picnic.   (123)

  8 Margie and her two sister-in-laws are spending a week in Chicago.   (86)

  9 It required twenty-five bucketsful of sand to fill Tim's sandbox.   (87)

10 The rooves of many of the old houses in Holland were made of tile.   (83)

11 Marys sisters-in-law gave her two new charms for her bracelet.   (117, 86)

12 The girls' coat was lying on the ground as she played ball.   (120)

13 The baby-sitter was alarmed when she heard the children's crys.   (122, 80)

14 Instead of turkey, we are going to have two gooses this Thanksgiving.   (84)

15 Mr. Jackson will furnish the turkies for the award banquet.   (81)

16 We are so pleased about Pat winning the scholarship to the university.   (127)

17 Julia, you will have to use somebody's else book until you find yours.   (126)

18 The five girl's mural was among the winners of the modern art contest.   (121)

19 Randee took both radioes and the record player to the repair shop today.   (79)

20 Dotty, your handwriting would be much neater if you would dot your *is*'.   (88)

21 I told Tom and Jo that we would meet them between the halfs of the game.   (82)

22 Mark bought a new sport coat at Brown's and King's Shop on Tenth Street.   (124)

23 The parent's group is meeting upstairs, and the teenagers' group is down here.   (121)

24 During her vacation, Barb is working in the childrens' shop at the Plaza.   (122)

25 My aunt has charge of the women's department in Lee and Jones' Shop.   (122, 120, 124)

37

SCORE _____ (Top Score 25)

Using Pronouns

If the italicized pronoun is correctly used, draw a line beneath it. If it is incorrectly used, write the correct form above it.

EXAMPLE: Joanna will go to the beach with Sue and *she*. (153)
                                                          her

1 Aren't Lee and Jody both much younger than *her*? (148)

2 Steve and *them* should be here soon with our picnic lunch. (149)

3 Sue is growing so fast that she must be nearly as tall as *me*. (148)

4 That howling dog wandering around the woods must have lost *it's* way. (146)

5 Send *whoever* will be able to deliver the message the quickest. (161)

6 I believe that Joe and he looked for *we* joggers in the wrong park. (157)

7 Roger and *her* will give their committee reports at the next meeting. (149)

8 The director gave Carl and *I* directions about our second-act entrance. (154)

9 Janet and Ned had planned to sit near Neta and *I*, but we got separated. (153)

10 Everyone in the class but Carlotta and *she* has a job during the summer. (156)

11 I am sure that Mrs. Turner will have enough room in her car for *we* girls. (157)

12 Julie is the aspirant *who* we believe will play the part of Lady Macbeth best. (159)

13 Do you think that we will be able to find Mark and *he* in this huge crowd? (153)

14 Alice brought the tickets and the cashbox to the booth for Louise and *I*. (153)

15 Is it *him* and Rose who are to represent Central High in the swimming meet? (152)

16 We will welcome *whoever* the principal chooses to be our graduation speaker. (162)

17 Was it *them* who decided that Barry would be a good candidate? (152)

18 All *us* students on the Student Council voted in favor of a party for the orphanage. (151)

19 Bob and *him* would like to play baseball with one of the major leagues someday. (149)

20 When Dad came home from Atlantic City, he brought *we* girls some salt-water taffy. (155)

Activity: How much can you learn about a word in a dictionary? Not only does the dictionary give every meaning of a word (some words have several meanings), but also it gives pronunciation, part of speech, derivation, standing as to usage (if below standard), syllabication, and often synonyms, antonyms, and other information of a general nature. Using your dictionary, list all the information you can find about the words **guerilla, meridian, symmetry, velocity,** and **villain.**

SCORE _____ (Top Score 20)

Pronoun Agreement

In each sentence write the correct pronoun for the antecedent given. Underline the antecedent of each pronoun that you write.

EXAMPLE: Students should take good care of ____*their*____ equipment.

1 Neither of the girls could find _____ skates.

2 Our debating team deserves _____ fine reputation.

3 Has each of the boys handed in _____ book report?

4 Each of the girls must furnish _____ own camping equipment.

5 Our band will wear _____ brand-new uniforms in the parade tomorrow.

6 Each of the classes should elect _____ officers by next week.

7 Each of the girls will have to make _____ own costume.

8 Each of the boys should be able to take care of _____.

9 The committee will give _____ report at the next scheduled meeting.

10 The police have returned each of the cars to _____ rightful owner.

11 One of the boys has left _____ history notebook in the principal's office.

12 Not one of the girls had remembered to bring _____ money for dues.

13 Neither Jane nor Sally will enter _____ dog in the contest.

14 Either Bob or Dick should bring _____ car if it is possible.

15 Has any boy asked for a change in _____ schedule of classes?

16 Both Jim and Joan passed _____ English IV tests without any difficulty.

17 Each of the boys worked as hard as _____ could on plans for the masquerade party.

18 The students who are in the public-speaking class are doing _____ best work.

19 Neither girl would lend _____ assistance when we had a flat tire.

20 Neither of the boys assumes the responsibility that _____ should.

21 No boy should fail to hand in _____ report on the day that it is due.

22 Any one of the women here will give you _____ opinion on part-time jobs.

23 Every one of the boys should do _____ best to make our guests feel welcome.

24 Every girl on the hockey team realizes that _____ will have to work hard to win.

25 The girls on the winning team will receive _____ awards at the end of the meet.

Plain English Handbook, 129, 130, 142, 163–165.

Activity: Write the declension of the personal pronouns. *Plain English Handbook,* 144.

SCORE _____ (Top Score 50)

39

Using Pronouns

In each sentence write the correct pronoun from within the parentheses.

EXAMPLE: The choice was between George and _____*me*_____ (I/me).   (153)

1 All the guests are here but Marilyn and _____ (her/she).   (156)

2 Gary is coming to the party with Jane and   _____ (I/me).   (153)

3 Jerry would not help Janet and _____ (I/me) fold the papers.   (272)

4 I believe that Kathryn is much younger than _____ (her/she).   (148)

5 Mother sent Margaret and _____ (me/I) a post card from Milan.   (154)

6 The coach is going with _____ (we/us) students to the picnic.   (157)

7 All _____ (we/us) acrobats have promised to perform at the carnival.   (151)

8 Was it _____ (they/them) who built the new house on the corner?   (152)

9 Sara repaired the typewriter for Jane and _____ (I/me).   (153)

10 Rod and _____ (they/them) are going to the circus next Saturday.   (149)

11 Was it _____ (she/her) who wrote the story that we liked so much?   (152)

12 Elena is the skier _____ (who/whom) we believe will win the race.   (160)

13 Is he the man _____ (who/whom) you saw at the florist's yesterday?   (160)

14 Was it Gene and _____ (he/him) who were coming early to help us?   (152)

15 It must have been _____ (she/her) who left the book on the radiator.   (152)

16 Rafael and _____ (he/him) have promised to make all the arrangements.   (149)

17 Appoint _____ (whoever/whomever) has the most time to do the work.   (161)

18 The stranger helped Steve and _____ (he/him) put up the top of the old car.   (272)

19 Are you sure that Marge and _____ (he/him) will go to the beach with us?   (149)

20 Will you show _____ (we/us) girls the pictures that you took on your trip?   (155)

Activity: Since the greater part of communication is supplied by conversation, the ability to converse intelligently and correctly is just as important as the ability to write in proper forms. *Plain English Handbook*, 642, lists some of the finer points in the practice of conversation. Read this section and write a paragraph on one of the points listed, such as "Be a Good Listener."

SCORE _____ (Top Score 20)

Reviewing Pronouns

Cross out each incorrect pronoun and write the correct form above it. If there is no incorrect pronoun, write **C** before the sentence.

EXAMPLE: It might be she who will bring the election results to Tom and ~~I~~ *me*.   (152, 153)

1   Robert and she are much taller than Joan and him.   (149, 148)

2   It must have been him who nominated Jean and her.   (152, 159, 153)

3   Helen and she are candidates whom we think will make good officers.   (149, 159)

4   All of we photographers must take care of our own equipment.   (157)

5   Either Eileen or Jane will bring their book for Fred and me.   (163, 153)

6   Uncle Charles gave Jack and I the tickets for all of us boys.   (154, 157)

7   Don and he have brought the stereo set upstairs for us girls.   (149, 157)

8   Larry and I saw Paul and she bicycling in the park yesterday.   (149, 153)

9   The principal and she divided the chores between George and I.   (149, 153)

10   Helen and them will go to see the principal with Peggy and me.   (149, 153)

11   All we sophomores have tickets to the ice show but Stan and she.   (151, 156)

12   Nan told Helen and me that every girl has handed in their report.   (154, 164)

13   Are you sure that it was him whom you saw get into the red cab?   (152, 160)

14   Sam and them will help Tom and him with the stage sets for the play.   (149, 153)

15   Marge and I have asked Miss Wilson to go with we girls to an art exhibit.   (149, 157)

16   All us boys like our counselor.   (151)

17   It couldn't have been they whom you saw with Jo and she last night.   (152, 160, 153)

18   Was it him who painted the picture that Hal and I saw in the window?   (152, 160, 149)

19   Every senior girl will do their best to help Ted and him with the new program.   (164, 153)

20   Every one of us boys knows that they should listen to the director and him.   (157, 163, 153)

41

Activity: Writing a précis, or condensation, of an article, story, or paragraph is an excellent method to use in developing the ability to write well. Study sections 557–560 in *Plain English Handbook* and then select the material that you wish to condense. Try to reduce the number of words to one-third or one-fourth of the original, but be sure to retain all the meaning of the original.

SCORE _____ (Top Score 20)

Reviewing Nouns and Pronouns

Cross out each incorrect noun or pronoun and write the correct form above it.

me   Hill
EXAMPLE: Jack will meet Don and ~~I~~ at ~~Hill's~~ and Bird's Restaurant.   (153, 124)

1 Was it him or her who hung up the men's and womens' coats?   (152, 122)

2 Is it she whom you say is more patient than me?   (152, 159, 148)

3 Are you sure it was him who you saw with us boys?   (152, 160, 157)

4 Whom did you say would take we hockey players out to the skating rink?   (159, 155)

5 All us juniors but Sara and she have already ordered our yearbooks.   (151, 156)

6 Whoever you appoint will work on the committee with Anne and me.   (162, 153)

7 Corina and me are going to have lunch on my sister's-in-law patio.   (149, 123)

8 It is him who you should send to the library with Hal and I.   (152, 159, 153)

9 It must have been them whom you saw talking with John and she.   (152, 160, 153)

10 It was not him who took the two boy's car without telling them.   (152, 160, 121)

11 Is it her whom you think deserves the scholarship to the university?   (152, 160)

12 Ed and me carried bucketsful of water to the pickers working in the fields.   (149, 87)

13 Take the tickets to whomever has volunteered to sell them for we girls.   (161, 157)

14 Have you heard of Ruth visiting Peg and she at a resort in Pennsylvania?   (127, 153)

15 It might have been her who arranged the swimming party for we girls.   (152, 159, 157)

16 The childrens' mother came to see Leah and I about baby-sitting with them.   (122, 153)

17 Was it him whom you wanted to go out to get sandwiches for us girls?   (152, 160, 157)

18 Each girl will do their best to help the club retain their tennis trophy.   (164, 165)

19 Al and me saw many elk when we visited his brother-in-laws in Wyoming.   (149, 89, 86)

20 Every boy should cast their vote for whomever will make the best chairperson. (164, 160)

Activity: When you are speaking on the telephone, the person to whom you are speaking has nothing to judge you by except your voice. Is yours a polite and pleasant telephone manner? Dramatize several different telephone calls with your classmates. You might call a friend who has been sick, make an airplane reservation, make an appointment with a doctor, or invite someone to a party. Have a period of criticism at the conclusion of each dramatization. *Plain English Handbook*, 644.

SCORE _____ (Top Score 40)

42

LESSON 33

Using Adjectives and Adverbs/1

To complete each sentence, select the better form of the adjective or the adverb from within the parentheses.

EXAMPLE: The tea tasted so ____sweet____ (sweet/sweetly) that I did not drink it. (289)

1 What _____ (kind of/kind of a) sports car was he driving? (307)

2 John is not _____ (so/as) eager to go to college as Billy. (310)

3 Gina plays tennis _____ (well/good) for a beginner. (329)

4 On the golf course you can beat me _____ (easy/easily). (339)

5 We couldn't find _____ (no/any) pictures that we liked. (336)

6 Ed is taller than _____ (any/any other) person in our class. (298)

7 Jo likes any of _____ (this/these) kinds of books, I am sure. (302)

8 This new recipe is not much different _____ (from/than) that old one. (337)

9 We _____ (sure/surely) had a good time at your luncheon party. (311)

10 I feel _____ (different/differently) about the book now. (289, 312)

11 We were _____ (most/almost) home when the storm broke. (328)

12 Of the two cities, isn't Salem the _____ (larger/largest)? (296)

13 Martha seems _____ (rather/sort of) unhappy today. (333)

14 Do you like _____ (those/that) kind of magazine? (302)

15 Mr. Kane let us omit the _____ (five last/last five) questions. (303)

16 I made _____ (less/fewer) errors on my test this time. (306)

17 I walked aimlessly, going _____ (nowhere/nowheres) in particular. (330)

18 Who is to take _____ (a/an) aptitude test today? (286)

19 Jody feels _____ (some/somewhat) better this evening. (334)

20 I think it is the _____ (best/better) of the two programs. (296)

Activity: Draw an arrow from each adjective or adverb you selected to the word it modifies.

Spelling List/5

advantages	preliminary	plateau	cozy	illustrate
welfare	conversation	ceremony	appearance	suspense
scientist	incidentally	social	earnest	requirements
future	mirror	miniature	recognition	impression
prairie	enormous	eventually	cashier	recognize
television	certificate	grandeur	glorious	definite
previously	declaration	rescued	musician	delinquents
foliage	volunteered	preferred	character	tomorrow

SCORE _____ (Top Score 20)

43

Using Adjectives and Adverbs/2

Make all necessary corrections in the use of adjectives and adverbs in the manner indicated in the example.

EXAMPLE: ~~That there~~ *That* boy ~~sure~~ *surely* has less ambition than any~~*other*~~applicant in the room.   (674, 311, 298)

1 Most of the youngsters feel kind of bad about missing the game.   (333)

2 She surely does write real well for one with so little training.   (311)

3 The warmed-over coffee smelled good, but it tasted bitterly.   (289, 312)

4 Mr. Kemp is planning to go to California for a ten-days vacation.   (299)

5 I thought our new shoes were alike, but yours are different than mine.   (337)

6 Hal is not as tall as Bob, but he is the heaviest of the two.   (310, 296)

7 Although the car ran good, we drove down the highway very careful.   (329, 311)

8 There were not as many students taking German last year as this year.   (310)

9 We were sure surprised that the leaves had changed color so sudden.   (311)

10 I polished Dad's car, and now it is shinier than any car on our street.   (298)

11 Helen feels badly because she is kind of behind in her studying.   (289, 312, 333)

12 I have heard that the last three stories in this new book are real good.   (303, 311)

13 Margaret speaks French most as good as a Parisian would speak.   (328, 329)

14 This movie is some different than the book from which it was adapted.   (334, 337)

15 The room looks beautifully with the furniture arranged different.   (289, 312, 311)

16 We are real glad that there are less car accidents happening every week.   (311, 306)

17 If he had talked different, he would have made more friends while he was here.   (311)

18 Both perfumes smell sweetly, but this is the sweetest of the two.   (289, 312, 296)

19 Don't you think the governor talked good on the television program last night?   (329)

20 I have read two new books, and I think *The Great Bridge* is the best.   (296)

21 He is not so tall as Ted, but he is the best basketball player of the two.   (310, 296)

22 Ed wasn't never able to get from gym to Spanish class by the time the bell rang.   (336)

23 A Swiss boy, a Korean girl, and a Italian boy are exchange students in our class.   (286)

24 Due to our safety engineers, there are less accidents of these kind every day.   (306, 302)

25 The attorney seemed sincere, and she spoke eloquent about the innocence of the man.   (311)

Activity: Draw an arrow from each adjective or adverb you corrected to the word it modifies.

SCORE _____ (Top Score 35)

44

Using Prepositions and Conjunctions

Cross out each incorrect preposition or conjunction and write the correct form above it.

EXAMPLE: Robert and I differ *with* ~~from~~ one another about music.   (360)

1 Is Will still angry with the television set?   (351)

2 Did that book say that John Keats died from tuberculosis?   (358)

3 The generous stranger seemed eager to part from his money.   (362)

4 The wind has blown your letter in back of the desk.   (363)

5 John was getting off of the airplane when we saw him.   (364)

6 I liked the movie, but it was quite different than the book.   (361)

7 We had hardly started on our trip than the accident occurred.   (384)

8 Mr. Potter will probably return from his vacation inside of a week.   (356)

9 The old man was angry at the boys who were teasing the dogs in the park.   (351)

10 Aunt Sarah still comes to see us on Sunday just like she always has done.   (372)

11 He is sure to fail his history exam except he spends more time studying.   (370)

12 Barbara isn't sure if she is going to Stanford University or to Columbia.   (381)

13 Although the twins look alike, they differ with each other in disposition.   (360)

14 Karen is practicing her swimming strokes exactly like the coach told her.   (372)

15 I never see your old house without I wish that you were still living there.   (371)

16 As we watched, the man jumped in the river from the bridge to save the boy.   (357)

17 I do not feel as we should be taking this road because it looks very rough.   (379)

18 Only one other person beside Jim knows of the surprise that we are planning.   (353)

19 I think the responsibilities should be divided evenly between the four girls.   (354)

20 The seniors differ from the juniors about a gift to the *school*.   (360)

21 During the storm last night, heavy rains fell among Atlanta, Macon, and Savannah.   (355)

22 It was an unhappy day for Jim Keath, hero of *Moccasin Trail*, when he parted with the Crow Indians.   (362)

23 At the age of seventeen, Benjamin Franklin arrived at Philadelphia with one silver dollar in his pocket.   (352)

24 Although she could neither see or hear, Helen Keller was graduated from Radcliffe College with honors.   (378)

25 I saw on television where the governor has called a special session of the state legislature.   (380)

45

SCORE _____ (Top Score 25)

LESSON 36

Reviewing Modifiers and Connectives

Cross out each incorrect adjective, adverb, preposition, or conjunction and write the correct form above it. If there is no incorrect word, write **C** before the sentence.

bad
EXAMPLE: Nan felt ~~badly~~ about the accident that she had caused.   (289, 312)

1 There are less seniors than juniors in our debating club this year.   (330)

2 People who are going nowheres always seem to be in a hurry.   (312)

3 Bob is some better today, but he still feels weak.   (334, 289, 312)

4 Tom does his work carefully, just like his older sister did.   (372)

5 This shirt is different from the one I bought last week.   (337, 361)

6 Francesca said that there wasn't no one at the station to meet her.   (336)

7 Craig doesn't know if the new museum is opening tomorrow or next Saturday.   (381)

8 The larger of the two beagle puppies has jumped off of the chair.   (296, 364)

9 Few people feel good when they get too much sun.   (289, 312)

10 Which do you think is the best of these two pictures of Joan?   (296, 302)

11 The coach feels badly whenever our teams do not play well.   (289, 312, 329)

12 If we divide the job between the four of us, we should get it done quickly.   (354)

13 Ellen would not go to bed except I agreed to read "Goldilocks" to her.   (370)

14 Ann and I always differ with one another on modern art.   (360)

15 She paints unusually good, but she has no interest in becoming an artist.   (329)

16 Fred ran swiftly to the edge of the ocean and plunged in the waves.   (311, 357)

17 You surely read in the paper where we are going to have a new school.   (311, 380)

18 We think that Joan plays ball most as well as her brother did last year.   (328, 329)

19 Surely Hal and he will finish the research and the report inside of a week.   (311, 356)

20 The older of the two boys looked doubtfully when I said they could go.   (296, 312)

Activity: Figures of speech are used in writing and in speaking to obtain a desired effect. The six main figures of speech are *simile, metaphor, personification, hyperbole, metonymy,* and *synecdoche.* Study Section 676–682 in *Plain English Handbook* and then write six sentences, using one of the figures of speech in each sentence. Find good examples of figures of speech in poetry and prose, and discuss them in class.

SCORE _____ (Top Score 20)

46

Reviewing Verbs, Nouns, and Pronouns

Cross out each incorrect verb, noun, or pronoun and write the correct form above it.

EXAMPLE: Was it *she* ~~her~~ who practiced with Kay and him?   (152)

1 Ted and I went to the play rehearsal and set near the front of the room.   (149, 204, 217)

2 Neither Nora nor she knows whether you was given the leading role.   (237, 260)

3 After we performers had rehearsed our dance, we laid on some benches to rest.   (151, 204, 217)

4 The principal and the play's director think that a hundred dollars are too much to pay for renting costumes.   (245)

5 Ms. Young is going to look at some of the costume designs that Bob and I drawed.   (149, 204)

6 Our director is one of those teachers who is always ready to help us students.   (241, 147)

7 Mr. Lamas, not the students, have asked Ed and him to get sandwiches.   (261, 272)

8 If I was she, I'd ask Carita and him to paint scenery for the play.   (256, 272)

9 Lou should send the program design to he, the chairperson of the program committee.   (157)

10 Mrs. Marsh, as well as some teachers, were at rehearsal when Gail and I arrived.   (236, 149)

11 Ms. Young and he are actors whom we think will do all they can for us amateurs.   (149, 159, 157)

12 All we girls but Liz and she were very pleased with our costumes.   (151, 156)

13 I helped Joe and him unpack and sort out three cartonsful of stage props.   (272, 87)

14 Neither Miss Yee-Ren nor the girls was here when Bill and I came.   (238, 149, 204)

15 Grace and she took the childrens' parts until the two children arrived.   (149, 122)

16 Could it have been them whom Joe and he saw backstage earlier today?   (152, 160, 149, 204)

17 Here comes Mr. Blake and the stage crew to set up for us performers.   (239, 157)

18 Every one of the stagehands are here to help Chuck and me with the scenery.   (246, 153)

19 Tom don't know for sure that it was they whom he saw in the audience.   (197, 152, 160, 204)

20 I am sure all we others of the cast are sadder than her that the play is over.   (151, 148)

47

SCORE _____ (Top Score 20)

LESSON 38

Reviewing Verb and Pronoun Agreement

Cross out each incorrect verb or pronoun and write the correct form above it.

were
EXAMPLE: The students, not the teacher, ~~was~~ in charge of the program.   (261)

1 Jane and her think it is me.   (149, 152)

2 Bacon and eggs are the only dish that Amanda can prepare.   (247)

3 Each of the boys play as if he alone was responsible for winning the game.   (242, 258)

4 Jack and me think that each of the groups should elect their own officers.   (149, 163)

5 All us spectators are proud that our team has won its last six games.   (151, 165)

6 Neither the girls nor John were interested in going to the fair with us.   (238)

7 Here comes Jay and the boys to go to the bus stop with Susan and I.   (239, 153)

8 Tod and he have gone, and there goes Miss Webb and the others now.   (149, 239)

9 A number of we boys was at the gym when the other team arrived.   (157, 244)

10 Hal and he think that she is the trainer who they met at the rodeo yesterday.   (149, 160)

11 Every girl knows that they must help the team maintain its good record.   (164, 165)

12 It was her who announced that each boy should bring their own lunch.   (152, 142)

13 Either Paul or she have gone to help Ellie and she bring the phonograph.   (237, 153)

14 Us friends know that Gail is one of those people who is always complaining.   (151, 241)

15 Neither he nor his parents think that ten miles are too far to go to a ball game.   (238, 245)

16 Peggy, as well as her brothers, were glad when her mother come home.   (236, 204)

Activity: Write five sentences in which you use the relative pronouns **who, whose, whom, whoever,** and **whomever.** Write the use of each relative pronoun above it in each sentence that you write.

Spelling List/6

tough	graduation	preference	strength	applause
Christian	undoubtedly	communicate	arrangement	antique
sanitary	ancestors	familiar	naturally	worry
wondered	stretched	friendship	desperate	universe
missionary	practically	profession	already	ascend
vaccine	eccentric	sociable	varied	moisture
gymnasium	inaugurated	hazards	annoyance	throughout
commission	appreciate	areas	splendid	applicants

SCORE _____ (Top Score 25)

Reviewing Verbs and Pronouns

To complete each of the following sentences, select a verb or pronoun from the group at the right of each sentence that is lettered the same as the blank.

EXAMPLE: Neither Don nor the girls ᵃ____*were*____ on the raft   ᵃwere/was

when Joe and ᵇ____*I*____ swam out. (238, 149)   ᵇI/me

1 Was it ᵃ_____ ᵇ_____ came out to the farm with   1 ᵃher/she   ᵇwho/whom

Marian and ᶜ_____? (152, 160, 153)   ᶜhe/him

2 If I ᵃ_____ saved my money, I could have ᵇ_____   2 ᵃhad/have

to Boston with Terry. (368, 204)   ᵇgone/went

3 All ᵃ_____ candidates have ᵇ_____ some cam-   3 ᵃwe/us   ᵇdid/done

paigning except Gary and ᶜ_____. (151, 216, 153)   ᶜhe/him

4 Joe and ᵃ_____ think that every girl on the crew will do   4 ᵃI/me

ᵇ_____ part. (149, 164)   ᵇtheir/her

5 There ᵃ_____ three of ᵇ_____ counselors who   5 ᵃwas/were   ᵇwe/us

ᶜ_____ to camp early. (239, 157, 216)   ᶜcame/come

6 Do you think it was ᵃ_____ who said that neither Dick   6 ᵃthey/them

nor he ᵇ_____ elected? (152, 237)   ᵇwas/were

7 ᵃ_____ you there when the coach, as well as the players,   7 ᵃWas/Were

ᵇ_____ applauded loudly? (260, 236)   ᵇwas/were

8 It is ᵃ_____ who ᵇ_____ to arrange the top shelf   8 ᵃhim/he   ᵇis/am

because he is taller than ᶜ_____. (152, 249, 148)   ᶜshe/her

9 We haven't ᵃ_____ Lynn since the window was   9 ᵃseen/saw

ᵇ_____ when she tried to ᶜ_____ it. (204)   ᵇbroke/broken   ᶜraise/rise

10 Tim and ᵃ_____ have already gone home, but one of the   10 ᵃshe/her

announcers ᵇ_____ still here. (149, 246)   ᵇis/are

49

SCORE _____ (Top Score 25)

Reviewing General Usage

Cross out each incorrectly used word and write the correct form above it. If there is no incorrect word, write C before the sentence.

EXAMPLE: Tod and I think that we will leave for home ~~inside of~~ *within* a week.   (356)

1 Does the coach object to us going with Frank and him?   (270, 153)

2 You shouldn't feel bad because you do not sing good.   (289, 329)

3 Is Jerry and Beth going in the boat with Paul and me?   (247, 153)

4 Tom, Jackie, and I will go in his father's-in-law boat.   (149, 123)

5 All us boys have our bus tickets except Joe and he.   (151, 153)

6 Ramona and he work in the mens' department of the same store.   (149, 122)

7 Frank and he cannot hope to succeed except they do good work.   (149, 370)

8 We organizers should have set this chair in back of the desk.   (151, 217, 363)

9 If some of us students would study different, we might have better grades.   (157, 311, 293)

10 This is the largest of the two melons, but it tastes bitter.   (296, 289)

11 Our principal is sure pleased that there are less students failing.   (311, 306)

50

12 Is it he whom you think works harder than Bill or me?   (152, 160, 148)

13 It might have been he whom you saw with Dorita and her.   (152, 160, 153)

14 Are you sure it was Bob and he who brought the letters to Bess and I?   (152, 160, 153)

15 All we students were pleased that our team wore its new uniforms.   (151, 165)

16 Could it have been her whom Hal and me saw with Kit and him?   (152, 160, 149, 153)

17 The coach does not know yet whom will go in the car with Ann and me.   (160, 153)

18 Every one of us students was proud of Tom's winning the trophy.   (246, 157, 270)

19 If I was she, I'd ask Lucilla and he to help with the planning.   (256, 153)

20 She is one of those persons who is always eager to help us students.   (241, 157)

Activity: Write a letter of thanks to someone who has entertained you at a party or who has sent you a gift. You may have to invent a situation, but make it sound real. *Plain English Handbook,* 617 and 619.

SCORE _____ (Top Score 25)

Reviewing Troublesome Usages

Cross out each incorrectly used word and write the correct form above it. If there is no incorrect word, write **C** before the sentence.

                  she   *they*   *are*

EXAMPLE: Jack and ~~her~~ said it is ~~them~~ who ~~is~~ to drive. (149, 152, 249)

1 How do you know that their team are the best of the two? (240, 296)

2 Mother, if you are really tired, lay down for a while. (204, 217)

3 Her friendliness, not her talents, make everyone like her. (261)

4 The first report was that he had died of exposure. (358)

5 The athlete strained to raise herself higher on the bar. (204, 217)

6 Georgia is not as likely to give in as John. (310)

7 Each boy must bring their own equipment for the camping trip. (164)

8 Those boys have been setting by the pool all afternoon. (204, 217)

9 Jim wants to learn me to play the drums. (227)

10 We should of gone home after the last inning. (230)

11 My two brother-in-laws are going to help me build a boat. (86)

12 Inside of a month I will be able to buy more records. (356)

13 She doesn't know yet if she will be able to go to Chicago with us. (381)

14 Each of the athletes were eager to go with the coach and I. (242, 153)

15 Us reporters find him to be one of those people who is very uncooperative. (151, 272, 241)

16 There go him and Shirley with Don and she. (239, 153)

17 The childrens' parents are planning a party for the holidays. (122)

18 No one wants to help them boys clean the garage. (168)

19 Linda reads good for a child of her age. (329)

20 All of we sophomores were proud of Sue winning the tennis match. (157, 270)

51

Activity: In formal writing, there are types of expressions which should usually be avoided. These inappropriate types are labeled **archaic, barbarisms, colloquialisms, improprieties, neologisms, provincialisms, slang, vulgarisms, hackneyed** (or **trite**) **expressions,** and **idiomatic expressions.** Study sections 654–664 in *Plain English Handbook* and make a list of several of each type.

SCORE _____ (Top Score 25)

Review of Reviews

Cross out each incorrectly used word and write the correct form above it. If there is no incorrect word, write C before the sentence.

EXAMPLE: We could ~~of~~ *have* finished this job today if we had begun yesterday. (230, 204)

1 There goes Henry and Herb outside to raise the flag. (239, 217)

2 If I were her, I'd use only two capsful of paint thinner. (152, 87)

3 Is Kate and Margot to help Ted and him with the program? (247, 153)

4 Mary and he danced good as a team and they looked wonderful. (149, 329, 289)

5 One of the skaters in the chorus of the ice show are staying with my cousin. (246)

6 There wasn't no one else with John and I when we saw the accident. (336, 153, 204)

7 That girl who came with Ed and me is the oldest of the two sisters. (160, 153, 296)

8 Although the boys played well, they feel badly because they were defeated. (329, 289)

9 Miss Grayson, not the girls, have asked Dan and me to help. (261, 272)

10 It was he who said that each of the girls brings her lunch. (152, 160, 163)

11 Could it have been them who were with Buck and her at the horse show? (152, 153)

12 Pat and he behaved so bad that Tom will not baby-sit with them again. (149, 311)

13 There was sixteen people in the chorus and they all sang beautiful. (239, 311)

14 Us students are surely making less errors in our grammar now. (151, 311, 306)

15 All of us girls know that our club has cause to be proud of their record. (157, 165)

16 Judy and I had done our work and had gone home when Nan came. (149, 204)

17 Neither Sal nor Lou were at Stone and King's Store when I got there. (237, 124)

18 Tom and her say it is them who are to go in their car with them. (149, 152)

19 It was they who hung up the men's and womens' coats at the party. (152, 122)

20 When we came, Antonio and he had gone somewheres. (330)

Activity: Write a letter of application for a part-time job that you have heard or read about. Remember that a letter of application is your first introduction to a possible employer and you want to make a good impression. *Plain English Handbook,* 590–603, 605.

SCORE _____ (Top Score 25)

Sentence Structure

This test parallels, in content, Inventory 4, page 109.

I. *Sentence Parts*
(Lessons 43–45)   20 Points

Indicate whether the italicized group of words in each sentence is a phrase or a clause by writing **P** or **C** before the sentence. On the line provided, rewrite the sentence, changing each phrase to a clause and each clause to a phrase.

EXAMPLE· _P_ The girl *swimming in the pool* is Jean.

_____ *The girl who is swimming in the pool is Jean.* _____

__ 1 *When the sound of the wind died*, silence was everywhere.
_____

__ 2 The woman *who is chopping wood* is Mrs. Chris.
_____

__ 3 *Realizing the humor of the situation*, Marty laughed with the rest of us.
_____
_____

__ 4 *When we visited Vermont last March*, we learned about maple sugaring.
_____

__ 5 *Thinking of the exciting day to come*, Suzie found it difficult to sleep.
_____
_____

__ 6 The snow *blowing around the buildings* looked ghostly.
_____

__ 7 *Driving into the garage*, Tom saw Ed's car.
_____

__ 8 *Anticipating a rain storm*, we took our umbrellas.
_____

__ 9 *Although Jo knew the job was temporary*, she accepted it.
_____

__10 *Because Lee arrived early*, she helped Mrs. Field.
_____

II. *Sentence Effectiveness*
(Lessons 46–50)   10 Points

Each item consists of two expressions of the same thought. Draw a ring around **A** or **B** to indicate which is the better sentence.

EXAMPLE: **A** Arranged on a corner shelf, Janet found the antique cups.
　　　　　　Ⓑ Janet found the antique cups arranged on a corner shelf.

1 **A** Pam is Mark's sister, and she is spending the summer in San Francisco.
　B Pam, Mark's sister, is spending the summer in San Francisco.

2 **A** Nancy saw a pants suit and a sweater in a shop window which she liked.

  B In a shop window Nancy saw a pants suit and a sweater which she liked.

3 **A** Standing on the hill, the autumn sunset was brilliant.

  B Standing on the hill, we saw the brilliant autumn sunset.

4 **A** Walking quickly, we reached home before the rain started.

  B Walking quickly, home was reached before the rain started.

5 **A** Sue told Kay that she had been elected president.

  B Sue said, "Kay, you have been elected president."

6 **A** Stan likes to read poetry, especially poems by Robert Frost.

  B Stan likes to read poetry. Especially poems by Robert Frost.

7 **A** When traveling in Italy, we enjoyed skiing in the Italian Alps.

  B When traveling in Italy, skiing in the Italian Alps was enjoyed.

8 **A** All the students had a good time. When they celebrated the victory.

  B All the students had a good time when they celebrated the victory.

9 **A** Sam is busy studying because he is going to take the college entrance examination.

  B Sam is busy studying. Because he is going to take the college entrance examination.

10 **A** The sophomores are working hard, decorating the gym for the dance.

  B The sophomores are working hard. Decorating the gym for the dance.

III. *Words in the Sentence*

(Lessons 51–54)

20 Points

Cross out each incorrectly used word and write the correct form above it.

                      come

EXAMPLE: Here ~~comes~~ the boys walking down the beach with Joanie and her.

1 All of my teammates thinks it is them who are to blame for losing the game.

2 There was some of we girls who did not think you were responsible for losing it.

3 As I came into the room, the famous world traveler raised to her feet and spoke.

4 Some one else had ought to help Kay and she carry the lunch down to the beach.

5 Louise and her should be back from Mexico City inside of a week, I believe.

6 This book is different than the other, but I think that it is the better of the two.

7 If I was he, I would go fishing, and there isn't no reason for his not going.

8 Could it of been she who we saw in the restaurant with Janet and him?

9 The coach and I are trying to learn Bill and him a new play.

10 Neither Bob nor Celia were at home when Hank and he went to see them last night.

11 Juliana is younger than she, and she surely does talk good for a two-year-old.

12 It was they who helped us drink nearly three pitchersful of lemonade at lunch.

13 Jake and he are the boys whom we think will help Jill and me at the rummage sale.

14 Neither the dog nor the cats was at the door to greet me when I came home.

15 Alice is much younger than he, but she makes less mistakes in French.

SCORE _____ (Top Score 50)

54

Phrases and Clauses

The italicized group of words in each sentence is either a phrase or a clause. On the lines provided, rewrite each sentence, changing each italicized phrase to a clause and each italicized clause to a phrase.

EXAMPLE: *When we toured the museum,* we saw many art treasures.
Touring the museum, we saw many art treasures.

1 Joe has often told us *of his longing to travel through Asia.*

2 *Waiting for the others to come,* Elaine and I played table tennis.

3 *As they walked along Fifth Avenue,* they looked in all the windows.

4 The player *who is at bat now* is Tony Perez.

5 *The girls just coming to camp* are eager to see the new pool.

6 The old cottage *that overlooks the ocean* is falling apart.

7 *As I watched television intently,* I let my plate drop to the floor.

8 The author, *encouraged by the literary critics' praise,* started another novel.

9 *After I washed the car,* I applied a coat of wax.

Plain English Handbook, 387–409, 422.

55

Spelling List/7

ambitious	boulevard	reservoirs	convince	daughter
superstition	delicious	interpret	assure	represents
afterwards	assortment	curious	frightened	bureau
revolution	scholars	primitive	research	cellar
possibility	phrase	caution	officials	financially
audience	continuous	reciprocate	fought	registration
valid	merchants	circular	reputation	exactly
immense	compelled	fortunate	obliged	recipes

SCORE _____ (Top Score 9)

Variety in Sentence Beginnings

On the first line classify the italicized beginning of each sentence by writing one of these symbols:

v for verb	**adj** for adjective	**part** for participial phrase
adv for adverb	**d c** for dependent clause	**prep** for prepositional phrase
	obj v for object of verb	

On the second line classify each sentence as to form by writing **S** for simple, **Cd** for compound, **Cx** for complex, or **Cd-Cx** for compound-complex.

EXAMPLE: ___*adv*___ ___S___ *Silently* the little boy slipped into the room.

_____ _____ 1 *While Dan and I were in England,* we had many interesting experiences.

_____ _____ 2 *Most* interesting perhaps was our tour of the Lake District.

_____ _____ 3 *Wearing a fisherman's knit sweater and carrying a walking stick,* Dan looked like a British walker.

_____ _____ 4 *Armed with a good map, a compass, and plenty of sandwiches,* we walked all day.

_____ _____ 5 *Treeless,* fog-covered mountains made the scenery solemnly beautiful.

_____ _____ 6 *Have* you ever been to the Rocky Mountains?

_____ _____ 7 *Much* smaller in scale than the Rockies, these British mountains are nevertheless beautiful, scenic, and rugged.

_____ _____ 8 *Narrow* footpaths took us over hills and into villages.

_____ _____ 9 *Boldly* we made some strenuous climbs; we saw wonderful waterfalls and lakes.

_____ _____ 10 *Having walked twenty-five miles in a day,* we felt we enjoyed our rest in a youth hostel.

_____ _____ 11 *Throughout our trip,* the weather was perfect.

_____ _____ 12 *Since we were both used to city living,* it was strange to walk from one village to the next; we had a new perspective on the countryside.

_____ _____ 13 *During our walk,* we'd meet and talk with other hikers.

_____ _____ 14 *Very* often, small animals like stoats crossed our path.

_____ _____ 15 *Sometimes* farm dogs would bark at us as we crossed farm fields.

_____ _____ 16 *Sitting on top of a mountain,* we felt strangely moved.

_____ _____ 17 *Reach* up, and you can almost touch the sky.

_____ _____ 18 *Memories* of this we will always have.

_____ _____ 19 *Also* enjoyable were our visits at the hostels.

_____ _____ 20 *As we looked back,* we thought of the interesting people from many countries we had met.

56

Plain English Handbook, 410–416, 422, 425–431.

SCORE _____ (Top Score 40)

Variety in Sentence Structure

On the first line classify the italicized group of words in each sentence. If the group of words is a clause, write **C**. If the group of words is a phrase, indicate the kind of phrase by writing **prep** if it is a prepositional phrase, **abs** if it is an absolute construction, **app** if it is an appositive, or **part** if it is a participial phrase.

On the second line classify each sentence according to its structure, or form, by writing **S** for simple, **Cd** for compound, **Cx** for complex, or **Cd-Cx** for compound-complex.

EXAMPLE: *The painting finished*, we drove out to the lake.	abs	S
1 Betty Morris, *who is my cousin*, is president of our class.	___	___
2 *The president being absent*, we did not have a meeting today.	___	___
3 Betty Morris, *the president of our class*, is my cousin; but I did not vote for her.	___	___
4 The girl *who is president* is Betty Morris; she is my cousin.	___	___
5 *That Betty Morris is president of our class* is not unexpected.	___	___
6 *On a beautiful autumn afternoon* Ichabod Crane rode to the party at the home of Katrina.	___	___
7 Ichabod was happy *as he rode toward the Van Tassel home*.	___	___
8 *Anticipating a delightful time*, the schoolmaster enjoyed the ride.	___	___
9 *The troubles of school forgotten*, he thought only of happiness.	___	___
10 Even Gunpowder, *the old horse*, responded to the beauty about him.	___	___
11 Marie Curie, *the famous scientist*, endured many hardships.	___	___
12 If you are discouraged by reverses, read the life of Marie Curie, *the discoverer of radium*.	___	___
13 *Refusing to accept misfortune*, she struggled on to discover radium.	___	___
14 Marie Curie, *who surmounted all obstacles*, richly deserved her fame.	___	___
15 *Waiting patiently for his master*, the dog stands by the gate.	___	___
16 *Although his master does not return*, the dog still waits.	___	___
17 The dog, *a faithful friend*, still waits for his master.	___	___
18 Laura Ingalls Wilder, *the well-known writer*, wrote stories that interest young people.	___	___
19 *Knowing the psychology of youth*, Laura Ingalls Wilder wrote much for boys and girls.	___	___
20 Laura Ingalls Wilder, *who was a well-known author*, wrote for young people.	___	___

Plain English Handbook, 99, 101, 389, 390, 396, 410–416, 421.

Activity: Write five sentences; then rewrite each, varying sentence structure as was done in this lesson.

SCORE _____ (Top Score 40)

57

Sentence Weaknesses

Each item in this lesson contains a confusing reference of a pronoun, a dangling verbal modifier, a misplaced modifier, a needless shift in person, number, or voice, or parallel thoughts not in parallel form. On the line provided, rewrite each item, correcting the weaknesses.

EXAMPLE: Every boy should do their own work.
Every boy should do his own work.

1 Don told Jack that he had been invited to the party.

2 We campers like to swim and playing tennis.

3 When we went camping, a good time was had.

4 Ruth saw a leather coat in a shop window that she liked.

5 Working hard, the job was finally completed.

6 Marilyn told Louise that she would be appointed chairperson.

7 We saw some places in New Mexico that we liked.

8 Standing on the hill, the sunrise was colorful.

9 Each one of the girls should bring their swimming suit.

10 Overcoming odds is heroic, but to give up is cowardly.

11 Each girl should work hard if they hope to succeed.

12 Planning great things is easy, but to do them is difficult.

13 Opening the door, a strange sight was seen.

14 We went to the party and a wonderful time was had.

15 In the winter I like to skate and playing basketball.

Plain English Handbook, 438, 439, 450–455.

SCORE _____ (Top Score 15)

58

Sentence Faults

Each item in this lesson contains a comma blunder, a run-on blunder, a period fault, or ideas of unequal rank joined by **and**. Rewrite each item to improve it. Try to subordinate lesser ideas (433, 447) rather than write primer sentences (449).

EXAMPLE: The speaker is here have you seen him?
The speaker is here. Have you seen him?

1 Lynda has a scholarship, she expects to attend Harvard next year.
_____

2 Our president has gone to the meeting he will bring us a report.
_____

3 Helen is on our debating team and she likes to listen to radio forums.
_____

4 Bob and I finished our work. While you and Jack were away.
_____

5 Mary Jane is a friend to everyone, all the students like her.
_____

6 Rolando always does good work. Because he wants to go to college.
_____

7 Betty won the race, and she is a good runner.
_____

8 Charlotte attends law school, and she plays in a dance band, and she earns her expenses.
_____

9 Tish likes biology she hopes to become a heart specialist.
_____

10 We enjoyed the afternoon. Especially the drive in the park.
_____

11 Roberta is a talented illustrator, and she is studying medieval art.
_____

12 Everyone will have a good time. When we go on the picnic.
_____

13 Ann writes poetry, and her brother is a reporter.
_____

14 The boys are working hard. Hoping to complete the job soon.
_____

15 Mary is the chairperson she will preside at the meeting.
_____

Plain English Handbook, 433, 436, 444–447, 449.

Activity: Explain the fault of each ineffective item above.

SCORE _____ (Top Score 15)

Reviewing Sentence Weaknesses

Each item in this lesson contains a defective sentence. The defects are caused by needless shifts in person or number or voice, by dangling verbal modifiers, by misplaced modifiers, by run-on blunders, by parallel thoughts not in parallel form, by incorrect uses of the comma or the period, or by confusing reference of a pronoun. Rewrite each item, making all changes necessary to correct sentence weaknesses.

EXAMPLE: Each boy must furnish their own ski equipment.

Each boy must furnish his own ski equipment.

1 Tom asked Dick if he thought he would be elected.

2 The new sweaters are here, have you seen them?

3 Rita thinks hiking is more fun than to bike.

4 Standing at the window, many people passed by.

5 Ellen has come have you seen her?

6 To fight for freedom is striving for the benefit of humanity.

7 The person who spoke was Gerald Myers he is our president.

8 Strolling through the woods, a waterfall was seen.

9 Hal Brown is our captain, do you know him?

10 Maria likes to write stories. Particularly historical stories.

11 We saw many things in the store that we wanted.

12 When we went fishing, many fish were caught.

13 Betsy and I stayed. Until the other women came.

14 If any boy wishes to take the course you must enroll now.

15 The coach likes to swim, he likes to skate, too.

Plain English Handbook, 438, 439, 444–446, 449–455.

Activity: Analyze one of the sentences which you have rewritten. *Plain English Handbook*, 412.

SCORE _____ (Top Score 15)

Capitalization and Punctuation/1

Insert punctuation marks where they are needed; cross out each incorrect mark and place the correct mark above it. Cross out each word that is incorrectly capitalized and write the correct form above it.

EXAMPLE: Lou Williams, a ~~Sophomore~~ *sophomore* in West ~~high~~ *High* School, is the soloist.   (500, 471)

1 Most of the Sophomores will study the following subjects History english and Geometry.   (471, 493, 504)

2 The Speaker quoted from "Four little foxes" the poem by Lew Sarett.   (478, 500)

3 As we listened the minister quoted from the bible and prayed for gods blessing.   (497, 477, 476, 519)

4 "Now is the time," the teacher said "when you should learn good english."   (503, 468)

5 The director said, Whenever you come come early.   (507, 506)

6 The president he is a senior said that the club would be self-supporting.   (526, 533)

7 When my brother goes back to College next Fall he will do graduate work.   (471, 470, 497)

8 "Why did you laugh," Mary asked, when he said Pardon me and sat down?"   (515, 501, 513)

9 The famous speaker began There is no—He did not finish the sentence.   (501, 507, 466, 522)

10 Sue and I went to Ripton Vermont last christmas we stayed a week.   (500, 469, 486, 464)

11 Peg met colonel Shaw while she was in Boise, Idaho last Spring.   (481, 500, 470)

12 Did Edgar Allan Poe receive only ten dollars for "The raven."   (478, 514, 529)

13 Ben asked his Mother whether he could go to mexico during may.   (482, 468, 469)

14 In 1986, the astronomy Club went to New Zealand to see halleys Comet.   (471, 484, 519)

15 I have never visited the southwest however I hope to someday.   (474, 490)

16 Did Dorothy Parker write "One perfect rose."   (478, 514, 529)

17 Our new teacher once taught in a High School in Atlanta Georgia.   (471, 500)

18 Was the battle of Gettysburg fought in the Revolutionary war.   (473, 529)

19 No my cousin doesnt work in the mens department of that store.   (498, 482, 517, 519)

20 did Whitman write the poem "when Lilacs last in the dooryard Bloomed."   (464, 500, 478, 514, 529)

61

Activity: Apply your knowledge of punctuation and capitalization to the writing of a paragraph. *Plain English Handbook,* 541–555.

SCORE _____ (Top Score 70)

Capitalization and Punctuation/2

The sentences in this lesson are defective as a result of incorrect capitalization and punctuation. Cross out each word that is incorrectly capitalized and write the correct form above it. Insert all necessary punctuation marks; cross out each incorrect mark and place the correct mark above it.

EXAMPLE: Ben has practiced all week, *hoping* ~~Hoping~~ to improve his backstroke. (446)

1 Harold is here now, he must have come with the coach. (444, 486, 490, 464)

2 I like football very much, what is your favorite game? (444, 486, 464)

3 We can play a game of quoits. While the others swim. (446, 497)

4 You should read this new book it is very interesting. (445, 486, 490, 464)

5 We saw many interesting places. When we were in the East. (446, 497)

6 Chris Jordan is captain of the team he is an excellent player. (445, 486, 490, 464)

7 The team entered the tournament yesterday. Expecting to win the trophy. (446, 499)

8 Bette swims well, she hopes to become an Olympic swimmer. (444, 486, 490, 464)

9 Robert will attend Princeton he will major in English. (445, 486, 490, 464)

10 I like swimming in the ocean some people do not like it. (445, 486, 490, 464)

11 Mary writes well, let her write the story for the paper. (444, 486, 490, 464)

12 This is the last game of the season we must not lose it. (445, 486, 490, 464)

13 Who brought these grapes they are very good. (529, 445, 464)

14 We returned from the long trip. Feeling that it had been worthwhile. (446, 499)

15 Mr. Weldon is our new music director, have you met him? (444, 486, 490, 464)

16 Our principal is in the East now. Attending an educational meeting. (446, 499)

17 Alice and Jane are here, the other students have gone. (444, 486, 490, 464)

18 My mother is a real friend she never fails me. (445, 486, 490, 464)

19 This is a good story, have you read it? (444, 486, 490, 464)

20 I like all kinds of flowers. Especially those that bloom all summer. (446, 499)

Activity: Study the punctuation and capitalization rules in section 464–540 of *Plain English Handbook*.

SCORE _____ (Top Score 40)

Using Verbs

Cross out each incorrect verb and write the correct form above it. If there is no incorrect verb, write **C** before the sentence.

EXAMPLE: Here ~~comes~~ *come* Jo and Terry, but they are too late.   (239)

1 One of the girls are here now, but the others have not come.   (246, 216)

2 Nan don't know whether or not the colors for the costumes have been chosen.   (197, 185)

3 Neither Claire nor Mike are here, but here comes Jane and Sue.   (237, 239)

4 A number of the employees was not here when we did that work.   (244, 216)

5 Neither Ann nor the boys was here when Dave and I come.   (238, 216)

6 The new club president, as well as the members, were glad we came.   (236, 216)

7 There was about ten students in the room when the bell rang.   (239, 204)

8 The others had gone to the pep rally when Tim and I come.   (204, 216)

9 The assistant coach, not the players, were here when we came.   (261, 216)

10 Fred give me this book on chess for you while you was in class.   (204, 260)

11 Each of the players act as if he was the captain.   (242, 258)

12 If I were Hank, I'd lay down on the grass and rest.   (256, 217)

13 If Jill was at the meeting, she has not spoken about what was done.   (257, 204)

14 Every one of the students are proud that our senior team have won the trophy.   (242, 240)

15 Neither Joe nor Ann has seen Jim since you was here at noon.   (237, 260)

16 That student don't know that she is to bring the dues to me.   (197)

17 If I was the chairperson, I'd invite everyone who is willing to work.   (256, 242, 249)

18 He is one of those people who is never satisfied with what they have done.   (241, 216)

19 Neither Mr. Howe nor the girls was here when the barbershop quartet sang.   (238, 204)

20 We had sat but a moment when the speaker rose and begun her address.   (217, 204)

Spelling List/8

enemies	universal	icicles	feature	monotonous
procession	feign	opposition	convenience	criticize
personally	project	forgotten	exhaustive	organized
excelled	citizens	excels	formally	qualify
orchestras	examinations	pageant	purchase	granite
commercial	readily	concrete	cooperate	opponents
gracious	exceptionally	necklace	faucet	reception
eminent	imaginary	congratulate	operators	quality

SCORE _____ (Top Score 25)

Substantives, Modifiers, Connectives

Cross out each incorrect noun, pronoun, adjective, adverb, preposition, or conjunction and write the correct form above it. If there is no incorrect word, write **C** before the sentence.

besides
EXAMPLE: There were four girls ~~beside~~ me who went swimming.   (353)

1 Helen looked proud, and she surely spoke good.   (289, 311, 329)

2 Was it Fred and him who sent the letter to we girls?   (152, 157)

3 Most of we other boys are taller than Mike and he.   (157, 148)

4 It was she and I whom you saw with Carlos and him.   (152, 160, 153)

5 Henry is some taller than me, but I am the heavier.   (334, 148, 296)

6 Sarah and she are the girls whom we think will help Tom and me.   (149, 160, 153)

7 Sue and she told Ann and I to mix two bucketsful of water with the cement.   (149, 272, 87)

8 Hal and him should have given the notes to me.   (149)

9 Jack played well, and there isn't no reason for him to feel bad.   (329, 336, 289)

10 The principal asked Joe and me to divide the money between the four boys.   (272, 354)

11 Rachel was angry at John for taking the bicycle without telling her.   (351)

12 I lost the badminton racket and couldn't find it anywhere.   (330)

13 Jane is not as good at swimming as Mary and me.   (310, 148)

14 Lucille and she expect to be back home inside of a month.   (149, 356)

15 This outline is different than the one you gave Hank and me.   (337, 154)

16 Elsa and he will not go to the picnic except Beth and I will go with them.   (149, 370)

17 If Hugh and he had behaved different, they might have been chosen.   (149, 311)

18 Neither of the judges thinks that this is the best of the two stories.   (163, 296)

19 Are you sure it was them who saw Kay and he at the rodeo?   (152, 153)

20 Every boy in the club will do their best to encourage Lana and him.   (164, 153)

21 It could have been they who you saw with Dave and her.   (152, 160, 153)

22 Frank and me will help Clair and her with the school radio program.   (149, 153)

23 Tim and I have asked Dad to go with we boys to the automobile show.   (149, 157)

24 Less than sixty people have enrolled for the new sewing classes.   (306)

25 We found our way to East High School easy last night.   (339)

Activity: Give the use and case of each substantive you corrected.

SCORE _____ (Top Score 30)

Reviewing Word Usage

Cross out each incorrectly used word and write the correct form above it. If there is no incorrect word, write C before the sentence.

EXAMPLE: That boy is ~~sort of~~ *rather* quiet, isn't he?   (333)

1   It could have been he whom you saw with Cindy and her.   (152, 160, 153)

2   Jack is the older of the two, and he surely does skate good.   (296, 311, 329)

3   Here comes Solar and she to help Paolo and I with this report.   (239, 149, 153)

4   Ted and he helped Anna and me pick twenty basketsful of apples.   (149, 272, 87)

5   Did the ancient Egyptians believe that the earth was round?   (251)

6   Should each girl bring their own canteen and sleeping bag?   (142)

7   It was she who told me that you was the leader for we boys.   (152, 260, 157)

8   The boy who you saw with me is my cousin from Maine.   (160)

9   As I come into the room, the woman who sat at the desk raised to her feet.   (216, 217)

10   He and I had drove a short distance when the rain began to fall.   (149, 204)

11   Elaine and she have done much better work than many people older than them.   (149, 148)

12   Is Joe and he going with my sister and I?   (149, 153)

13   John Ross is the older of my two brother-in-laws.   (296, 86)

14   Gene and he sit in back of me in our English class.   (149, 217, 363)

15   Sue and he should of helped James and her with the plans.   (149, 230, 153)

16   There are less cheerleaders this year, but they surely have spirit.   (306, 311)

17   The men's lifes are very routine.   (122, 82)

18   It was us boys who wanted to leave early.   (151)

19   Madeline told us to give out the ten last books.   (303)

20   There goes the girls now with Mrs. Raines and him.   (239, 153)

21   Bill and he think it is me who is to blame for the error.   (149, 152, 249)

22   If I was she, I'd ask Marie and him to have some new games.   (256, 272)

23   Neither Kay nor Jorge were here when he and I came to class.   (237, 149, 216)

24   Sam is one of those people who is always talking at the wrong time.   (241)

25   The coach and he were greatly pleased at us winning the big game.   (149, 270)

65

Activity: Give the reason for each correction you have made.

SCORE _____ (Top Score 30)

Review of Reviews

Cross out each incorrectly used word and write the correct form above it. If there is no incorrect word, write C before the sentence.

lives

EXAMPLE: Do you enjoy reading about the ~~lifes~~ of famous people? (82)

1 If I was she, I'd ask Hugh and her to go with Bess and him. (256, 272, 153)

2 Hal and her saw Ruth and he when they came into the room. (149, 153, 216)

3 It could of been Kay who you saw with Susan and him. (230, 160, 153)

4 After we had did most of the work, Don and he came to help us. (216, 149)

5 The younger of those two boys surely plays handball good. (296, 311, 329)

6 Henry and he say there isn't no one to go with Ray and me. (149, 336, 153)

7 My assistants and I have filled the orders; the drivers have went to deliver them. (149, 216)

8 When we boys ran to the corner, we seen the wrecked cars. (151, 216)

9 The coach is trying to learn George and him a new play. (227, 153)

10 There was four boys who had done their work and had gone home. (239, 216)

11 It must have been her who came to the party with Ann and him. (152, 216, 153)

12 Elena and she will go with Jim and me to the show tomorrow. (149, 153)

13 Fred is really the better athlete of the two, but he don't like hockey. (296, 197)

14 We students know that each of the boys will do their part to win. (151, 163, 242)

15 Ms. Ward is one of those teachers who is eager to inspire we students. (241, 157)

16 Each of the musicians think that I am responsible for the booking. (242)

17 There are many of us who do not think you was to blame for the error. (239, 260)

18 Was Don and she here when Ken and he came? (247, 147, 216)

19 Five hundred dollars were paid to Mr. Ford for his share of the property. (245)

20 Jaime don't seem as tall as his younger brother. (197, 310)

21 You would soon get well if you would only do like the doctor ordered. (372)

22 Mother had us children lay down for a nap every day when we were small. (155, 217)

23 Some of us boys had ought to help Dick and her with the luggage. (157, 225, 153)

24 Miss Wilson and he had not given us all the instructions when the bell rang. (149, 216)

25 We girls had eaten breakfast and had began our work when Tim and he come. (151, 204, 216)

SCORE _____ (Top Score 30)

Composition and the Use of Words

This test parallels, in content, Inventory 5, page 111.

I. *Paragraphs, Outlines, and Letters*
(Lessons 55–60)

15 Points

Underline the bold-faced word or phrase that makes the statement true.

EXAMPLE: In dialogue each speech is (**set off by dashes**/<u>**separately paragraphed**</u>).

1 The sentences of a good paragraph are (**loosely/closely**) related in thought.
2 The topic sentence of a paragraph is (**always/generally**) at the beginning.
3 The proper arrangement of the sentences in a paragraph is (**emphasis/coherence**).
4 Unity in the paragraph means (**sticking to the subject/proper arrangement of parts**).
5 The topics of an outline should be arranged in (**no special/logical**) order.
6 The most careful writers use (**many/few**) abbreviations in letters.
7 End punctuation is (**necessary/optional**) after the salutation and close of a letter.
8 The date is the (**first/last**) item of the heading.
9 Expressions such as *beg to say* are now considered (**effective/obsolete**).
10 The mark usually placed after the salutation of a business letter is the (**comma/colon**).
11 The mark usually placed after the salutation of a friendly letter is the (**dash/comma**).
12 The participial closing is (**omitted/much used**) by modern writers.
13 (**Each/Only the first**) word of the complimentary close is capitalized.
14 The signature should be followed by (**no punctuation/a period**).
15 The business letter has (**five/six**) parts.

II. *Faulty Expressions in the Sentence*
(Lessons 61 and 62)

10 Points   67

Cross out each faulty expression and write above it the correct or more appropriate one.

EXAMPLE: What kind of ~~affect~~ *effect* did the ocean have on you?

1 If I go any farther with the plans, the other members will be angry.

2 My cousin is a real talented musician.

3 It will be a long ways for those girls to walk.

4 Didn't almost all the boys suspicion him of stealing the ball?

5 Because the bridge was out, that was all the farther we could go.

6 Not a one of them knew what was wrong with the car.

7 Do you know where Mother put the peanuts at?

8 Neither of the three girls could think of an answer.

9 His words of warning are likely to effect their actions.

10 Bob will let you have his car if it is alright with his father.

III. *Using Words in the Sentence*
[Lessons 64–66]

Cross out each incorrect word and write the correct form above it. If there is no error, write **C** before the sentence.

EXAMPLE: Nell and ~~her~~ *she* picked several bucketfuls of apples.

1 Although Sarah is angry at you, you shouldn't feel bad.

2 Doesn't he know how the thieves was captured?

3 Here come Fred and Bill with Mary and she.

4 Invite whomever will help Ruth and her.

5 Although the pie didn't look well, it tasted good.

6 Neither her gloves nor her coat were different from mine.

7 June is one of those workers who is never satisfied.

8 The president, not the members, are responsible.

9 If she was you, she would sit down and say nothing.

10 He cannot do differently except we help him.

11 As the boat sunk, the crew swam to the island.

12 It was probably they who left us boys the tickets.

13 As soon as I seen him, I gave him your message.

14 You was here when she told us about Betina's entering the contest.

15 The sun had already raised when we ate breakfast.

16 Neither Alice nor Ann would lend their book.

17 Do you feel that you can do like we do?

18 Was you there when Jack and I came?

19 Are Joe and Bert coming with Diane and she?

20 Doris and she surely feel bad about it.

21 Except you come, Jake is likely to stay at home.

22 I am sure that whomever you invite will go with Tom and him.

23 The taller of the two lamps is the best one to use while reading.

24 All us seniors bought our sweaters at Howell and Dunn's store.

25 Was it he whom you helped?

68

SCORE _____ (Top Score 50)

Paragraph, Précis, and Outline

Underline the bold-faced word or phrase that makes the statement true.

EXAMPLE: There are (six/<u>four</u>) types of expression known as forms of discourse.   (551)

1 A paragraph develops (**only one topic/several topics**).   (541)

2 A topic (**may/may not**) be developed in more than one paragraph.   (541)

3 In dialogue each speech is (**separately paragraphed/set off by dashes**).   (542)

4 One sentence (**always expresses/does not always express**) the topic.   (544)

5 The topic sentence is placed (**at the end of/anywhere in**) the paragraph.   (544)

6 There (**is only one way/are many ways**) to develop a topic.   (545)

7 Giving stress to important ideas in a paragraph is called (**emphasis/coherence**).   (550)

8 Sticking to the subject is called (**emphasis/unity**).   (548)

9 The correct arrangement of sentences in a paragraph is (**unity/coherence**).   (549)

10 The form of discourse used in explaining is called (**description/exposition**).   (552)

11 Picturing in words is called (**description/narration**).   (553)

12 The form of discourse used in telling a story is (**argumentation/narration**).   (554)

13 A précis is (**more/less**) precise than a paraphrase.   (558)

14 A good précis retains (**none/all**) of the thought of the original.   (558)

15 Précis writing is good for those who use too (**few/many**) words in writing.   (559)

16 A good précis (**retains/changes**) the order of the thought of the original.   (559)

17 In writing a précis, one should use (**one's own words/the words of the original**).   (559)

18 Clear and forceful sentences are (**optional/necessary**) in précis writing.   (558)

19 The topics in an outline should be arranged in (**irregular/logical**) order.   (578)

20 The main topics of an outline are marked by (**Roman numerals/Arabic numbers**).   (579)

69

Activities: Practice in the writing of précis is an excellent aid in developing the ability to write well. Read 557–560 in *Plain English Handbook,* and then select a short article you wish to condense. Try to reduce the number of words to one third of the original word count. Retain all the meaning of the original text. Write a paragraph on the value of knowing how to write good letters.

SCORE _____ (Top Score 20)

Letter Writing

Underline the bold-faced word or phrase that makes the statement true.

EXAMPLE: The business letter has (**five**/<u>**six**</u>) parts. (590)

1 Letters are broadly divided into (**four**/**two**) general classes. (586)
2 A letter (**may**/**may not**) combine both business and social purposes. (586)
3 A business letter (**need not be**/**should be**) answered promptly. (589)
4 The heading should be at the upper (**left-hand**/**right-hand**) side of the paper. (591)
5 Careful letter-writers abbreviate (**little**/**much**) in headings. (591)
6 The date is the (**first**/**last**) item in the heading. (592)
7 The inside address of a business letter is placed (**at**/**near**) the left margin. (594)
8 The inside address may be omitted from a (**social**/**business**) letter. (617)
9 End punctuation is (**required**/**not required**) in the heading and inside address. (593)
10 The (**heading**/**inside address**) contains the address of the writer. (591)
11 The salutation should be below the inside address (**near**/**at**) the left margin. (595)
12 The form of the salutation (**should**/**need not**) be consistent with the type of letter. (595)
13 If the word *dear* is preceded by the word *my* in a salutation, both words (**are**/**are not**) capitalized. (596)
14 A close such as *I remain* is now considered (**effective**/**obsolete**). (599)
15 The (**comma**/**colon**) is used after the salutation of a business letter. (597)
16 The (**comma**/**dash**) is properly used after the salutation of a friendly letter. (617)
17 The style of a letter of friendship should be (**conversational**/**formal**). (617)
18 A good business letter (**should**/**need not**) be clear, concise, and courteous. (589)
19 (**Each**/**Only the first**) word of the complimentary close is capitalized. (599)
20 The participial closing is (**never**/**much**) used by the best writers. (599)
21 The only mark used after the complimentary close is the (**period**/**comma**). (599)
22 The signature should be written (**legibly**/**with a flourish**). (600)
23 The signature (**may**/**may not**) be typed beneath the longhand form. (600)
24 The informal invitation follows the form of the (**social**/**business**) letter. (617)
25 The formal invitation is always written in (**first**/**third**) person. (623)

70

Spelling List/9

audio	mobilize	economy	siege	quarantine
mediator	unsaturated	intimate	medieval	symbol
scientific	mezzanine	permanent	immaterial	characteristic
metropolitan	queue	consistent	quotient	persuasion
Hawaiian	apricot	acceptance	catastrophe	resources
jovial	apparatus	individual	substitutes	inadequate
vertebra	tariff	criticism	lenient	marvelous
apropos	medium	invalid	device	prophecy

SCORE _____ (Top Score 25)

The Business Letter

Make all necessary corrections of the letter parts. Insert needed punctuation marks, and correct errors in spelling and capitalization by crossing out the incorrect word and writing the correct form above it. If something is in the wrong place, indicate the correct position by arrows.

May 10 19____

537 Crestway Ave.

Clarksville Nebraska 68005

Mr George J. Holmes

1735 East Grand street

Lincoln, Neb. 68508

Dear Mr. Holmes;

I read in the *clarksville chronicle* that you were looking for a sound technicien when Sherlock and the holmes Gang goes on it's east Coast tour this summer. I would like you to consider me for the job.

I am eighteen years old and a senior at Clarksville high. I have been in charge of Sound at School assemblies and for three musicles produced in school. I have also played bass for the past two years in a local band, the Marbles. We have played at high school dances throughout the county.

I would like to work for your band, first of all, because I admire it. Second, Im seriously interested in a career as a sound engineer, and the experience would be very helpful. I want to major in communications in College and hope to work for a college radio station.

I can give you references on reguest.

I'd be happy to see you for an intervew at your conveneince.

Yours Very Truly,

Robert Gordon

Robert Gordon

Plain English Handbook, 468, 470, 471, 474, 478, 481, 487, 500, 502, 591–595, 597–600.

Activity: Write a business letter. Select the type of letter you wish to write from the list in *Plain English Handbook*, 604.

SCORE ________ (Top Score 25)

The Letter of Inquiry

Make the necessary changes in capitalization, punctuation, spelling, and usage to correct the letter.

1	110 south Main Street
2	Madison Wisconsin 53702
3	November 5, 19____

4   Mr. Hank Christopher

5   230 Randal Road

6   Belmont California 94002

7   Dear mr. Christopher:

8   The Percy high school Band is going to hold an auction on saturday afternoon

9   April 23. Our goal is to raze money for new uniforms. If you remember what they

10   were like when you were here you'll agree that we need them. Our cheif auction item

11   is a rare record you made when you were still a student here that is why

12   Im writing.

13   Since you will be giving a concert in madison that weekend, we was wondering

14   if you would auction off the record yourself? Most everyone at school are a fan of yours.

15   Your being at the auction would certinly draw the crowd we need for a successful auction.

16   If you are interested, please drop us a note. We would gladly work the

17   auction around your busy skedule.

18   Yours truely

19   *Frances Bauer*

20   Frances Bauer
            President, Percy high school Band

Plain English Handbook, 164, 197, 204, 217, 328, 464, 468, 469, 471, 481, 486, 487, 494, 497, 500, 502, 529, 591, 600.

Activity: Write a letter of inquiry. Read *Plain English Handbook,* 607, for information concerning the letter of inquiry. Study 589–603 for the requirements and correct form of the business letter.

SCORE _____ (Top Score 25)

The Friendly Letter

Make the necessary changes in capitalization, punctuation, and usage to correct the letter.

1   Parkdale camp

2   Clear lake minnesota 55319

3   July 15 19——

4 Dear Beverly

5   This is certainly the most peculiarest camp I've ever saw.

6 When I arrived, I couldn't believe dad talked me into it. Its a

7 camp for computers! I mean, it's for kids, but we learn how to

8 program computers. This may not sound like the typical sort of

9 camp but it's really not that different after all. The food is

10 still terrible, so I know it's a true-blue summer camp. In addition,

11 there is hiking swimming and other sports, besides computer Programming.

12   The computers are more interesting than I thought they would

13 be. Some of the kids have devised some real clever computer games.

14 We can play the games without spending bagsful of quarters the

15 way we do at tom's pizzeria. Dad suggested I come here because he

16 thought programming would be a kind of good thing to learn if I'm

17 still interested in a career in Math. Beside, he can be very con-

18 vincing when he starts lecturing on the importance of doing different

19 things he's gotten me into more stranger situations than this one!

20   I've made some friends here. Jeff is a <u>brain</u> but a very funny

21 person. Linda reminds me of you she's a sci-fi nut, too. We hope to

22 program a computer to do most all of our homework next year.

23   Have a good time on your trip. I'll see you this Fall back

24 at central High school.

25   Love

26   Marla

73

Plain English Handbook, 87, 197, 204, 216, 239, 246, 294, 295, 311, 328, 333, 353, 464, 468, 470, 471, 474, 482, 495, 496, 497, 500, 502, 517, 531, 593, 600, 617.

SCORE _____ (Top Score 32)

The Letter of Congratulation

This note of congratulation contains errors in capitalization, punctuation, usage, and spelling. Correct the errors.

1   475 Riverview drive

2   Livermore Falls Maine 04254

3   May 26 19____

4   Dear Roberta:

5   It wasn't no surprise to me to read in the evening paper where

6   you have just recieved a Summerfield Scholarship. Your hard work in

7   Junior and Senior High School has brought you this honor, which you

8   so well deserve. I am especially pleased to know that your scholastic

9   record alone did not win this here award for you. Your exemplary char-

10   acter and pleasing personality was contributing factors, I am sure.

11   Although I hope to see you soon I felt like I had ought to write

12   tonight to express my congratulations to you. I wish you every success

13   in the four years of College that the scholarship provides. You are

14   one whom I think will make the most of this opportunity, and I predict

15   great success for you in you're Engineering program.

16   Sincerely Yours

17   *Tom Brooks.*

Plain English Handbook, 146, 160, 225, 247, 336, 372, 380, 468, 471, 473, 484, 497, 500, 517, 591–601, 617, 622, 674.

Spelling List/10

anonymous	vermin	cemetery	considerably	counterfeit
conciliate	lethargy	referendum	encyclopedia	forcible
eminent	emphatic	laboratory	maneuver	perspiration
heritage	conceivable	minimum	reversible	picnicking
journalism	decorum	acquaintance	inflammable	susceptible
leotard	aggravate	bachelor	masquerade	hypocrite
refrain	treasurer	definition	principally	effective
subordinate	artificial	changeable	superfluous	syndicate

SCORE _____ (Top Score 25)

Faulty Expressions in the Sentence/1

In the following sentences are expressions that should be replaced by more appropriate words for formal writing. Cross out each faulty or incorrect expression and write the correct form above it.

EXAMPLE: Not a̶ ̶o̶n̶e̶ of us knew about it.
                        one

1 My father's family reared hogs on a farm near Topton, Pennsylvania.

2 His testimony in court is liable to effect the jury.

3 He doesn't know that it is only a little ways to the main highway.

4 We were awful tired; therefore, we could walk no further.

5 Although Bob is not so credible as Sue, he is easily fooled.

6 None of the four children wanted farther work in the garden.

7 Most all the girls have finished their work.

8 She would not let me say anything farther about the matter.

9 He drives that car good for one who has just learned.

10 The mayor greeted less people formerly at this year's reception than at last year's.

11 It was surely funny that the criminal gave himself up.

12 I expect he is not so well informed as Jim.

13 Gloria did not suspicion that Joan was angry with her.

14 Why don't you set here while I try to fix the car?

15 I suspect that Ann will teach you to play backgammon.

16 We suspicioned him of telling a lie.

17 The roads are liable to be in bad condition after the rain.

18 We'll get up a social evening for the new members with invites like you suggested.

19 Do you feel that it is alright for me to go now?

20 He ate his meal like he hadn't had anything to eat for a week.

Plain English Handbook, 665–674.

75

SCORE _____ (Top Score 25)

Faulty Expressions in the Sentence/2

In the following sentences cross out each faulty or informal expression and write above it the form that would be appropriate in formal writing.

likely

EXAMPLE: If we boys work hard, we are ~~liable~~ to succeed.

1 How did the announcement effect that woman in the corner?

2 I expect you know that Doris is angry with us.

3 Isn't it funny that Jane should feel so bad about it?

4 Tom and Mike met an interesting party at a ranch in New Mexico.

5 I expect his uncle will learn him more about the business.

6 We are hoping that the leaders will be able to affect a compromise.

7 Where is he aiming that rifle at?

8 Doesn't he live further from school than I do?

9 No one would ever suspicion Bert of doing a dishonest thing.

10 I expect Harold is mad because I wouldn't lend him my pen.

11 This book is torn alright; it looks badly.

12 Not a one of us thought it was warm enough to go swimming.

13 We can ride altogether on our bicycles.

14 We officers had ought to discuss this topic farther.

15 I expect that Ann will go out as soon as she arrives in New York.

16 Most all of us want to proceed farther with the matter.

17 John can speak real well.

18 She was enthused about her trip to Japan and China.

19 We wanted to make sure that everything was alright before we left.

20 We expected Fred to conduct the games, but he had to stay to home.

Plain English Handbook, 665–674.

SCORE _____ (Top Score 25)

76

Punctuation and Capitalization Review

Make all necessary changes in punctuation and capitalization to correct the sentences. Each item properly marked counts two points.

The
EXAMPLE: We drove to Mexico. ~~the~~ highways were good all the way.   (445, 486, 464)

1 That author writes unusually good stories I have read many of them.   (445, 486, 464, 490)

2 We parked at the airport. Expecting their plane to arrive momentarily.   (446, 499)

3 This is a perfect fall day for a picnic, everyone should be here.   (444, 486, 464)

4 We ought to do it now this might be our last opportunity.   (445, 486, 464, 490)

5 Miss Albright writes amusing limericks, she is very talented.   (444, 486, 464)

6 Margarita is always punctual, some students are always late.   (444, 486, 464)

7 Our superintendent is a noted educator, have you ever met her?   (444, 486, 464)

8 Terry is one of my best friends, she is in my history class.   (444, 486, 464, 490)

9 Jack and I went swimming. While the other boys fished.   (446, 497)

10 Ralph hopes to win a scholarship, he is surely working hard.   (444, 486, 464, 490)

11 Fred is studying very hard now. Hoping to pass the next test.   (446, 499)

12 The children always liked the games. Especially the outdoor games.   (446, 499)

13 Ricardo is sure to win the prize. Because he always does his best.   (446, 497)

14 Ann and I pitched horseshoes. Until the others came.   (446, 497)

15 We surely had a good time, you should have been there.   (444, 486, 464)

16 Allen is planning the charity bazaar, he will tell us about it.   (444, 486, 464)

17 Helen is going to Yale next year, where are you going to college?   (444, 486, 464)

18 Miss Dorn is the advisor for our class, she is always ready to help anyone.   (444, 486, 464, 490)

19 We are all working hard these days. Realizing that our opportunity is great.   (446, 499)

20 Rita da Costa is a very intelligent girl, do you know her?   (444, 486, 464)

77

Activity: Classify each sentence as **simple, compound,** or **complex.**

SCORE _____ (Top Score 39)

Using Words: General Review/1

Make all necessary corrections in the use of words in this lesson.

EXAMPLE: The *smaller* smallest of the two boys is the *older* oldest.   (296)

1   I cannot guess whom it was unless it was him.   (159, 152)

2   Was you there when we heard about Shirley selling her story?   (260, 127)

3   Us girls will welcome whoever you and her are recommending.   (151, 162, 149)

4   That old car of our's is certainly different than their's.   (146, 337)

5   The players, as well as the director, is eager to begin rehearsal for the new show.   (236)

6   Tell me about Barbara winning the prize for her latest childrens' storys.   (127, 122, 80)

7   The two Henries fed several handsful of carrots to the donkies.   (80, 87, 81)

8   We couldn't hardly hear her, but we could tell that she was mad.   (336, 671)

9   These kind of light bulb are better than that there kind.   (302, 197, 674)

10   Neither Sally or Lana have written to we girls.   (378, 237, 157)

11   They had ought to teach us the correct use of those difficult verbs.   (225)

12   If I had only knew that you had no ride, I would of taken you.   (204, 230)

13   My cousin begun the program with a guitar solo.   (204)

14   There goes Jack and her in their brother's-in-law sports car.   (239, 149, 123)

15   Dick is doing some better in his work, but he still is not doing very good.   (334, 329)

16   Most all of we students will agree with the principal's plan.   (328, 157, 350)

17   The large and small calendars is on the library wall.   (305, 248)

18   Either the girls or Miss Garcia are to go with Tomás and I.   (238, 153)

19   The team is to receive its new sweaters before the next game.   (240, 165)

20   Was the turkies roosting on the rooves of the sheds?   (197, 81, 83)

21   He should return the dictionary to Fred and I.   (153)

22   The number of new students enrolling in our school this year are great.   (244)

23   My sister-in-laws receive high salarys as engineers for this states' new project.   (86, 80, 120)

24   He is one of those persons who always tries to be different than others.   (241, 337)

25   His aunt and uncle's eyes are blue, but his fathers' eyes are brown.   (125, 120)

SCORE _____ **(Top Score 55)**

Using Words: General Review/2

Make all necessary corrections in the use of words in this lesson.

EXAMPLE: The cake didn't ~~raise~~ *rise* very well, but we ~~eat~~ *ate* it anyway. (217, 204)

1 Was the penknife broke when you give it to Bob and he? (204, 216, 153)

2 It was her who met Jane and I at the airport. (152, 153)

3 Don and her give the horse two bucketsful of oats. (149, 204, 216, 87)

4 If you was the principal, what would you advise we students to do? (256, 155)

5 Them carpenters surely need any kind of work bad. (442, 311)

6 She done it exactly like her advisor told her to do it. (204, 216, 372)

7 Our teacher gave she and I extra credit for our special conservation project. (154)

8 Bob and her sure draw different than the other students. (149, 311, 337)

9 Was you here when Joan come to get the cherrys? (260, 204, 216, 80)

10 John brought five bushels of potatos from his two brother-in-laws' farm. (78, 86, 123)

11 It must have been her who done the painting on display. (152, 204, 216)

12 All us girls was in Brown's and Lane's Store today. (151, 197, 124)

13 We were surprised to learn of Tom winning the largest of the two prizes. (270, 296)

14 Neither Esther or Nell were in science class today. (378, 237)

15 Twenty-five dollars are too much to pay for that kind of felt hat. (245)

16 It must have been him and her who you met outside. (152, 149, 160)

17 We are liable to have less failures this semester than last. (671, 306)

18 Has Clara and her sister went to the meeting yet? (247, 204, 216)

19 Is it Sonya or me who were picked? (152, 197)

20 If I was him, I should invite whomever would come. (256, 152, 161)

21 Why don't you and her set with Grace and I? (149, 204, 217, 153)

22 Each man who you ask should bring their own lunch. (160, 142)

23 She had ought to learn us to do them problems. (225, 227, 168)

24 Don't he think that the criminal is guilty? (197)

25 There sits the guides who we seen at the natural history museum. (239, 160, 204, 216)

79

SCORE _____ (Top Score 59)

Using Words: General Review/3

Make all necessary corrections in the use of words in this lesson.

EXAMPLE: The boys, not ~~her, is~~ *she are* arranging the club's transportation.   (149, 261)

1 Him and her cannot succeed in this venture except we help them.   (149, 370)

2 She felt real glad about Jim winning the music award.   (311, 270)

3 The child fell off of the pier and in the deep water.   (364, 357)

4 It could have been them who were thought to be us.   (152, 274)

5 If Harry don't agree with we boys, we may leave him stay to home.   (197, 157, 227, 674)

6 A eagle is a large predatory bird who can fly very high.   (286, 141)

7 The youngest of the two children seemed sort of shy and timid.   (296, 333)

8 Jane does not know if she can vote or not, but she does agree with our plan.   (381, 350)

9 Us girls thought you to be she.   (151, 273)

10 Was Marie and her sister with you and he at the game?   (247, 153)

11 Divide the peaches between the four children to learn them to be fair.   (354, 227)

12 Our freshman football team have won all their games this year.   (92, 240, 165)

13 The lifes of the heros was always in danger.   (82, 78, 197)

14 Is it us girls whom you think should make the plans?   (151, 160)

15 There comes Don and Carlo with them girls who we met yesterday.   (239, 442, 160)

16 Mother will not leave us lay on the bed except we take off the spread.   (227, 204, 217, 370)

17 If I was her, I should do like I was told.   (256, 152, 372)

18 There isn't no time for us boys to set here in idleness.   (336, 204, 217)

19 No one beside Mr. Snyder knowed of our plans.   (353, 204)

20 You and her should of excepted the invitation.   (149, 230, 228)

21 Each of the boys were there to do their share of the clean-up work.   (163, 246, 142)

22 Had the bell already rung when you and he come to class?   (204)

23 She feels badly because her story is not as good as Janes.   (312, 310, 120)

24 Most all the money was divided between Ellen, Arthur, and I.   (328, 354, 153)

25 Each of the new women have done good in selling their tickets.   (163, 246, 329, 142)

SCORE _____ (Top Score 60)

Vocabulary Study/1

Here is an exercise to give you practice in detecting meaning from context (696). The sentences in the exercise are taken from magazine articles. The words that may be unfamiliar to you are italicized. The context for each word is only a sentence or two, but it should be enough to give you a clue to meaning. On the lines provided, write what you think the italicized words mean. Check your definitions by consulting the dictionary (686).

1 When a bear got into the cattle range, they dogged him *relentlessly* until they tracked him down or drove him deep into the wilder regions where the cattle never ranged.

_____

2 Someone from the other side of town, aware of Rocky's even disposition, tried to *goad* him into losing his temper during a football game.

_____

3 To keep the fishing boats from slipping through and laying mines required the Task Force to maintain a constant *vigil*, day and night.

_____

4 I was *skeptical*, for I just couldn't believe that so many brilliant, stationary fireballs could appear in such a concentrated area in so short a period.

_____

5 The differences between the original and the forgery are so slight as to be almost *imperceptible* to anyone except an expert.

_____

6 Mr. Messer's *antipathy* toward bears and his willingness to do them violence are shared by a dozen of his cattle-raising neighbors.

_____

7 Even the most renowned playwrights are not *immune* to the caustic criticism of newspaper reviewers.

_____

8 The nightmare of the railroads is financial collapse. As things stand now, the railroads are plunging downhill toward *insolvency*.

_____

9 There is much air traffic that we cannot do much about. Clearly we must not *tamper* with military flights.

_____

10 Once the minerals of this desert state were *depleted*, it had little chance of prosperity and hardly enough people to maintain a state government.

_____

SCORE _____ (Top Score 10)

Vocabulary Study/2

Our English word *migrate* means "to go from one place to another." Once you learn this word, it is easy to learn words related to it: *migration, migrant, migratory, immigrate, immigrant, immigration, emigrate, emigrant, emigration.* If you learn words ten at a time instead of one at a time, you can build a vocabulary easily and rapidly.

We borrowed the word *migrate* from the Latin word *migratus* ("transferred"). The prefix *im* means "in" and *e* means "out." We have borrowed thirty to forty percent of our words from Latin. If you learn just a few of these Latin words, you can learn hundreds of words built from them. You can learn words at even a faster rate than ten at a time.

Five Latin roots are listed below. (In language study a *root* is the base of a word.) The meaning of each root is given. Then several of the English words built from the root are listed. Your teacher may have you supply more examples and then check the derivations in the dictionary.

Latin Roots

Root	Meaning	English Derivatives
aud, audit	hear	audience, auditorium, audible
fac, fact, fect, fic	do, make	factory, defect, efficient
scrib, script	write	describe, subscribe, manuscript
spec, spect	look, see	inspect, spectacular, spectacles
tract	draw, pull	tractor, extract, subtract

The English derivatives given as examples are all familiar words. Other derivatives for the Latin roots may not be in your vocabulary. Write the meaning of each derivative. Use your dictionary if necessary. Your teacher may call upon you to use the words in sentences.

82

aud, audit
1 audition _____
2 audiometer _____
3 auditory _____

fac, fact, fect, fic
4 proficient _____
5 facile _____
6 facsimile _____

scrib, script
7 inscribe _____
8 scribble _____
9 prescription _____
10 circumspect _____

spec, spect
11 spectral _____
12 spectator _____

tract
13 protract _____
14 retract _____
15 traction _____

SCORE _____ (Top Score 15)

Vocabulary Study/3

One of the best ways to build a vocabulary is to develop an interest in words. That is what the writer of this essay has done. Words to her are a source of humor, too.

Dictionary Double Talk

With almost twenty thousand words to remember, I certainly can't be blamed for mixing up one or two once in a while, can I? I'm sure that if my vocabulary were composed of two or three hundred words, I'd not make the slightest error. Never, never would I have said, "Oh, Jane, don't be obese!" when I meant "obtuse"; I should not now be blushing to recall that once I told our pastor that a guest speaker certainly had a belligerent voice, when actually I thought it was benevolent.

I used to wonder about possible connections between words that sounded alike. Did people call a sale of odd, useless things a bazaar because all the things sold there were so bizarre? If so, would it follow that a magnate was one who made magnets? This seemed logical, for I had heard news commentators mention steel magnates quite frequently. I abandoned my theory, however, when I learned that pears grew one on a stem and not in pairs.

It is sometimes difficult to change words from negative to positive form. Why is not a well-mannered person no longer "couth," if one with poor manners is uncouth? Why doesn't a capable person do things "eptly," if a clumsy person does them ineptly? Changing from positive to negative presents some weighty problems, too. I'm sure, for instance, that something which is not sincere is called insincere, but, illogically, the word meaning "not flammable" is certainly not *inflammable*. Likewise, immoderate means "without moderation," but *impassioned* is not synonymous with "without passion."

Please, oh please, will someone solve my utter dilemma about chickens? Why on earth is undressing them called "dressing"? — RAE BERG, East High School, Rockford, Illinois

To appreciate the humor of "Dictionary Double Talk" you must know the meaning of the words the writer mentions. This lesson will test your knowledge of these words.

Underline the word or phrase that means the same or nearly the same as the italicized word. Use the dictionary to check your answers.

1 *obese* — a) slow, b) very fat, c) well-dressed, d) very thin

2 *obtuse* — a) clumsy, b) out of date, c) plain, d) stupid

3 *belligerent* — a) flippant, b) hostile, c) loud, d) sad

4 *benevolent* — a) kind, b) cruel, c) sarcastic, d) sharp

5 *bizarre* — a) expensive, b) old, c) fantastic, d) cheap

6 *magnate* — a) person of industrial prominence, b) public civil officer, c) one skilled in magic, d) magnet manufacturer

7 *flammable* — a) slow to burn, b) gaudy, c) shiny, d) easily set afire

8 *inflammable* — a) slow to burn, b) gaudy, c) shiny, d) easily set afire

9 *impassioned* — a) lacking passion, b) emotionless, c) full of passion, d) violent

10 *synonymous* — a) musical, b) artificial, c) opposite, d) alike

SCORE _____ **(Top Score 10)**

Vocabulary Study/4

Each sentence may be completed in five different ways. Underline the phrase that best illustrates the meaning of the italicized word in each sentence.

1 One thing to do with a *knoll* is (a) shoot it, (b) sweep it under the rug, (c) report it to the police, (d) save it to show your grandchildren, (e) climb it.

2 A *passé* sport (a) requires a great deal of skill, (b) is played outdoors, (c) can be played at any season, (d) is out of date, (e) is outlawed in this country.

3 The best thing to do with a *mandate* is (a) eat it, (b) wear it, (c) throw it away, (d) obey it, (e) put it in the bank.

4 A *loquacious* person (a) sings well, (b) is silent, (c) is talkative, (d) travels a lot, (e) wears a uniform.

5 A person on a *pinnacle* (a) is on the bottom rung of a ladder, (b) has gone about as high as possible, (c) is living in a dream world, (d) sleeps on a featherbed, (e) is impatient because of the excitement.

6 The place for a *coronet* is (a) in the magazine rack, (b) in a jazz band, (c) in a cigar store, (d) on the dining-room table, (e) on the head.

7 If something is *negligible*, you might (a) take it to the cleaners, (b) easily disregard it, (c) shower it with attention, (d) invest it, (e) send it back to the factory.

8 A person of tremendous *girth* has (a) a large waist measure, (b) a lot of money, (c) great influence, (d) the intelligence of a genius, (e) an unlimited supply of energy.

9 A *coherent* person (a) talks logically, (b) can carry a tune, (c) babbles senselessly, (d) always seems in a hurry, (e) will eat anything.

10 A person who goes off on a *tangent* (a) takes a boat, (b) rides two on a bicycle, (c) strays from the subject, (d) gets angry, (e) goes on a fruit diet.

Circle each of the two words that are similar in meaning in each of the following groups. Underline the two words that are opposite in meaning.

EXAMPLE: (appetizing) approximate bold modest (tasty)

1 eminent filthy immaculate imminent impending

2 appearance crime openness semblance stealth

3 economical frugal prevalent scarce wild

4 deadly fatal cheerful injurious somber

5 acid alkaline temporary timely transient

6 figuratively literally literary particularly specifically

7 preventative precarious precipitous safe steep

8 cumbersome fast heavy mobile stationary

9 cheat coquette flirt master menial

10 exotic foreign prodigal runaway thrifty

84

Vocabulary Study/5

On the line at the left write the letter of the word or word group that means the same or nearly the same as the italicized word.

___ 1 *nettle* — (a) small patch, (b) trap for insects, (c) fine cord, (d) prickly plant, (e) young bird

___ 2 *chafe* — (a) make sore by rubbling, (b) poke fun at, (c) separate seeds from husks, (d) use a razor, (e) change course

___ 3 *aghast* — (a) disgusted, (b), eerie, (c) stern, (d) speechless, (e) horrified

___ 4 *mien* — (a) baseness, (b) one's self, (c) manner, (d) claim, (e) whim

___ 5 *fluctuation* — (a) overflowing, (b) healthy growth, (c) nervous confusion, (d) coming in of the tide, (e) changing back and forth

___ 6 *insinuate* — (a) do wrong, (b) hint, (c) insult, (d) falsify, (e) turn inside out

___ 7 *inter* — (a) go inside, (b) bury, (c) come between, (d) write, (e) rip

___ 8 *perennial* — (a) unmarried, (b) like a parent, (c) talkative, (d) lasting, (e) incidental

___ 9 *appraise* — (a) inform, (b) shower with compliments, (c) estimate the value of, (d) think something over, (e) move upward

___10 *saunter* — (a) stroll, (b) dampen, (c) wind around, (d) show off, (e) lag behind

___11 *vaunted* — (a) bragged about, (b) leaped over, (c) made useless, (d) jeered at, (e) overpriced

___12 *stratagem* — (a) semiprecious stone, (b) layer of rock, (c) measuring instrument, (d) trick, (e) court session

___13 *supersede* ___ (a) leave off, (b) overpay, (c) replace, (d) go out of bounds, (e) snub

___14 *citadel* — (a) palace, (b) fortress, (c) wooded valley, (d) city dweller, (e) stringed instrument

___15 *zenith* — (a) radio wave, (b) high point, (c) garden flower, (d) metalworker, (e) old person

___16 *sunder* — (a) make a loud noise, (b) sell various small items, (c) become warm, (d) divide, (e) shock

___17 *disconcert* — (a) sing out of tune, (b) inconvenience, (c) put an end to, (d) confuse, (e) act independently.

___18 *guile* — (a) cunning deceit, (b) responsibility for a crime, (c) workers' union, (d) Dutch coin, (e) mask

___19 *remonstrate* — (a) explain again, (b) pay for services, (c) plead in protest, (d) bloom another season, (e) increase in size

___20 *potentate* — (a) honorary title, (b) conquered territory, (c) court decree, (d) druggist, (e) powerful ruler

___21 *protrude* — (a) trespass, (b) stick out, (c) draw out, (d) object to, (e) investigate

___22 *impunity* — (a) evil intention, (b) sincere conviction, (c) light-heartedness, (d) lack of modesty, (e) freedom from punishment

___23 *prate* — (a) talk foolishly, (b) plea prayerfully, (c) be sorry, (d) put off, (e) sob

___24 *deign* — (a) pretend, (b) prefer, (c) refuse, (d) tiptoe, (e) condescend

___25 *psyche* — (a) disease, (b) circle, (c) mind, (d) beautiful woman, (e) insane person

SCORE _____ (Top Score 25)

Vocabulary Study/6

At the left of the number write the letter of the word or phrase that is most nearly **opposite** in meaning to the italicized word.

___ 1 *balk* — (a) unwind, (b) stop, (c) continue, (d) jerk, (e) waste

___ 2 *hapless* ___ (a) unfortunate, (b) capable, (c) lucky, (d) well-planned, (e) risky

___ 3 *inherent* — (a) apart from, (b) belonging to, (c) senseless, (d) not long enough, (e) not remembered in a will

___ 4 *privy* — (a) without a prayer, (b) known to all, (c) unofficial, (d) private, (e) of little importance

___ 5 *abashed* — (a) continuous, (b) unharmed, (c) blushing, (d) embarrassed, (e) self-confident

___ 6 *antagonism* — (a) forethought, (b) opposition,(c) weakness, (d) agreement, (e) hope

___ 7 *apprehensive* — (a) uneasy, (b) unafraid, (c) unwise, (d) free, (e) loud

___ 8 *depreciate* — (a) refuse to apologize, (b) make light of, (c) increase in value, (d) give back to, (e) do one's duty

___ 9 *dubious* — (a) doubtful, (b) good, (c) prejudiced, (d) guileless, (e) sure

___10 *infallible* — (a) liable to error, (b) without hesitation, (c) giving an incorrect impression, (d) held in low esteem, (e) always correct

___11 *copious* — (a) dry, (b) happy, (c) abundant, (d) scanty, (e) unduplicated

___12 *covert* — (a) secret, (b) greedy, (c) brace, (d) hopeful, (e) open

___13 *pallid* — (a) weak, (b) colorful, (c) alive, (d) upright, (e) inartistic

___14 *perturb* — (a) clean, (b) upset, (c) waken, (d) connect, (e) calm

___15 *momentous* — (a) far-reaching, (b) lasting, (c) inactive, (d) trivial, (e) immediate

___16 *inexorable* — (a) yielding, (b) undying, (c) prayerful, (d) airy, (e) relentless

___17 *chastise* — (a) taint, (b) become silent, (c) reward, (d) discipline, (e) lead

___18 *chronic* — (a) severe, (b) of short duration, (c) mild, (d) sudden, (e) cheerful

___19 *crude* — (a) elegant, (b) rough, (c) raw, (d) tasteless, (e) mature

___20 *impious* — (a) reverent, (b) ungodly, (c) sober, (d) slow, (e) graceful

___21 *encumber* — (a) heap together, (b) dislodge, (c) add to one's load, (d) attach no blame, (e) afford relief

___22 *languid* — (a) indifferent, (b) solid, (c) vigorous, (d) unattractive, (e) short

___23 *puny* — (a) without humor, (b) playful, (c) clean-smelling, (d) strong, (e) weak

___24 *feasible* — (a) undutiful, (b) impracticable, (c) hard, (d) possible, (e) sensible

___25 *belated* — (a) made glad, (b) early, (c) delayed, (d) lamented, (e) grumbled about

SCORE _____ (Top Score 25)

Vocabulary Study/7

The first two words form a pair. Find the word that makes a similar pair with the third word. Write the letter of this word at the left of the number.

EXAMPLE: _d_ wedding march : wedding : : dirge : (a) parade, (b) dance, (c) christening, (d) funeral, (e) battle

___ 1 smile : frown : : benediction : (a) worry, (b) prayer, (c) curse, (d) silence, (e) mumbling

___ 2 heat : thermostat : : fuel : (a) gas pedal, (b) steering wheel, (c) ignition, (d) carburetor, (e) brake

___ 3 nocturnal : night : : diurnal : (a) wakefulness, (b) moon, (c) day, (d) darkness, (e) light

___ 4 solar : sun : : lunar : (a) earth, (b) moon, (c) star, (d) planet, (e) satellite

___ 5 hitching post : horse : : quay : (a) automobile, (b) travel, (c) train, (d) pier, (e) ship

___ 6 wine : dregs : : river : (a) flood, (b) banks, (c) course, (d) sediment, (e) turbulence

___ 7 wholesome : health : : morbid : (a) disease, (b) food, (c) medicine, (d) mind, (e) psychology

___ 8 person : idle : : land : (a) sallow, (b) hallowed, (c) fallow, (d) callow, (e) shallow

___ 9 hot : cold : : volatile : (a) airy, (b) stable, (c) hazy, (d) underground, (e) cool

___10 spark : fire : : impetus : (a) fall, (b) ascent, (c) end, (d) argument, (e) motion

At the left write the letter of the word that best completes the sentence.

EXAMPLE: _b_ Much to my _____, I forgot the only line I was to speak and just had to stand there, red-faced. (a) surmise, (b) chagrin, (c) derision, (d) deportment, (e) retribution

___11 The operations officer thinks the fog will _____ before long and that we will take off on schedule. (a) disrupt, (b) dissent, (c) dissipate, (d) diverge, (e) distill

___12 He comes from a _____ family of middle-class, conventional shopkeepers. (a) Bohemian, (b) bourgeois, (c) socialistic, (d) productive, (e) proletarian

___13 It was a _____ crowd she addressed—people of all ages and all classes. (a) motley, (b) homogeneous, (c) illiterate, (d) disinterested, (e) spellbound

___14 Mr. Bly's decision will be a _____ one, because he is a wise and experienced person. (a) prejudiced, (b) tentative, (c) judicious, (d) peremptory, (e) patriotic

___15 Molly's description was so _____ that I felt as if I were seeing the sight myself. (a) grisly, (b) emotional, (c) vehement, (d) veritable, (e) graphic

___16 Howard is a _____ person, and I fear he will seek revenge. (a) deranged, (b) vindictive, (c) dumfounded, (d) zealous, (e) versatile

___17 The _____ stained-glass windows of the old cathedrals are lovely, but for the windows of our homes we want transparent glass. (a) translucent, (b) ornate, (c) luminous, (d) opaque, (e) expensive

___18 When the humidity is 100 percent, the air is _____ with water vapor. (a) sated, (b) distilled, (c) abounding, (d) saturated, (e) lavish

___19 You are no one's slave: you need not be _____ to anyone. (a) servile, (b) indebted, (c) obligated, (d) remorseful, (e) liable

___20 The singer always has a number of people hovering about him, like a prince with his _____. (a) delegation, (b) tribunal, (c) retinue, (d) menagerie, (e) auxiliary

SCORE _____ (Top Score 20)

Vocabulary Study/8

On the line at the left of the number, write the letter of the word or phrase that means the same or **nearly** the same as the italicized word. If there is no correct answer, write **X** on the line.

___ 1 *allocate* — (a) change location, (b) speak, (c) distribute, (d) approve, (e) unite

___ 2 *pallor* — (a) a dance, (b) a column, (c) an election, (d) a disease, (e) paleness

___ 3 *oblivious* — (a) restricted, (b) objectionable, (c) happy, (d) an angle, (e) forgetful

___ 4 *absurdity* — (a) that which is foolish, (b) that which is hateful, (c) that which is unsuccessful, (d) that which is profound, (e) that which is allowed

___ 5 *urban* — (a) country, (b) city, (c) sophisticated, (d) an acid, (e) study of stars

___ 6 *terrain* — (a) a turtle, (b) the sky, (c) the end, (d) a patio, (e) a tract of ground

___ 7 *blandishment* — (a) gentleness, (b) flattery, (c) a dessert, (d) imperfection, (e) fiction

___ 8 *butte* — (a) an animal, (b) an argument, (c) strike, (d) the end of a cigar, (e) a steep hill

___ 9 *legume* — (a) a vegetable, (b) a disease, (c) an insect, (d) a lawyer, (e) a body of soldiers

___10 *cascade* — (a) a steep waterfall, (b) a tree, (c) a wig, (d) a mountain, (e) a window

___11 *defunct* — (a) cheated, (b) challenge, (c) deceased, (d) degraded, (e) pay

___12 *skittish* — (a) extremely lively, (b) a small battle, (c) a short play, (d) sudden shower, (e) trickery

___13 *blasphemy* — (a) wonderful, (b) a skin disease, (c) a church official, (d) profanity, (e) indifference

___14 *arid* — (a) eager, (b) wet, (c) silly, (d) serious, (e) airy

___15 *banter* — (a) a large feast, (b) a diet, (c) a large flag, (d) good-natured ridiculing, (e) a stairway railing

___16 *stationary* — (a) sculpture, (b) growth, (c) law, (d) not moving, (e) writing paper

___17 *captivate* — (a) to take a prisoner, (b) fascinate, (c) to lead, (d) to capture a prize, (e) to overturn

___18 *alms* — (a) nuts, (b) fruits, (c) charitable gifts, (d) trees, (e) wealth

___19 *superfluous* — (a) magical, (b) the best, (c) miraculous, (d) expensive, (e) surplus

___20 *affront* — (a) gratify, (b) frighten, (c) trouble, (d) astray, (e) offend

___21 *chasm* — (a) a helmet, (b) a gorge, (c) a hunter, (d) a steep hill, (e) punishment

___22 *vehicle* — (a) furious, (b) a business enterprise, (c) a channel, (d) an opening, (e) a chamber of the heart

___23 *credulous* — (a) growing, (b) increase in sound, (c) climbing iron, (d) a sideboard, (e) inclined to believe

___24 *aversion* — (a) an escape, (b) greed, (c) an object of love, (d) the study of dirigibles, (e) dislike

___25 *archipelago* — (a) a mountain range, (b) mainland, (c) a church official, (d) a group of islands, (e) an archeologist

SCORE _____ (Top Score 25)

Vocabulary Study/9

The following sentences are taken from magazine articles. Read each sentence and try to figure out the meaning of the italicized word from the context. On the line provided, write what you think the word means. Check your answer in the dictionary.

1 Without the green of plants, the red-blooded animals of this earth could not exist, for virtually all forms of life draw their *sustenance* from green plants.

_____

2 The youngster showed a quick and engaging humor, a companionableness which at times *obliterated* the twenty years' difference in their ages.

_____

3 The other type of animal coloration due to physical structure is *iridescence*, just like that of oil films floating on water, or of soap bubbles.

_____

4 It was a friendly meeting, and all concerned hoped that relations would be even more *amicable* in the future.

_____

5 We have just completed a picture showing the trials and *tribulations* of an average letter carrier—all the obstacles that must be hurdled before the mail can finally be delivered to your door.

_____

6 The progress of life is *devious*, traveling in erratic and surprising ways to reach unexpected ends.

_____

7 As their final number at the concert, the rock group sang a *medley* of their most popular songs.

_____

8 Prior to the July, 1969 moon landing, many *simulated* flights to the moon were conducted by the Air Force.

_____

9 Most early space exploration was conducted by *proxy*; robots were sent into space instead of human beings.

_____

10 The explorers of the past required courage, but astronauts who have ventured into space have been *intrepid* indeed.

_____

SCORE _____ (Top Score 10)

Vocabulary Study/10

In the following selection there are several words that may be unfamiliar to you. However there are good context clues to the meanings of most of the words. First read the selection through. Then match the italicized words with the definitions in the list below the selection. Write the number of the italicized word on the line before its definition. Use your dictionary whenever necessary.

If you want to know what it feels like to be [1]*flayed* alive, you should try being an extemporaneous speaker. Do you know what that is? You're given a topic and expected to deliver a [2]*lucid* speech on it after a few minutes' preparation.

I was entered into an extemporaneous speech contest shortly after joining the [3]*Forensic* League in school. My much admired, though [4]*eccentric* English teacher admitted that I didn't have enough experience, but he thought it would be good for me. He said I had an [5]*intrinsic* talent for that sort of thing. When I replied that I'd rather be in a Roman [6]*amphitheater* facing fifty [7]*predatory* lions, he answered [8]*callously*, "Come, come, Tina. When I think how [9]*glib* you were when you explained why you hadn't finished your term paper—"

"All right," I cried [10]*petulantly*. "Blackmail, I believe, is the most [11]*despicable* crime."

So that's how I found myself among a group of [12]*fanatically* well-prepared speech students. I was given a [13]*prosaic* little topic—grain sales between the U.S. and the Soviet Union. My knowledge of the subject was [14]*infinitesimal*, but I went forward with an [15]*adamantine* spirit. I stood up and smiled [16]*obsequiously* at the judges. I tried to look as if I were [17]*deliriously* happy to make an [18]*impromptu* speech on the subject. My face [19]*emanated* pure joy. I began with a clever [20]*epigram*. Then I blushed—I didn't want to be too [21]*ostentatious* about my vast knowledge. For five minutes, I sputtered some [22]*muddled* nonsense. My speech was—by forensic standards—[23]*atrocious*. Believe me, it was not the [24]*apex* of my speaking career.

____a A circular building with tiered rows of seats surrounding an arena

____b Inclined to show off

____c Easily understood

____d Hateful

____e Dull

____f Belonging to the very nature of a thing

____g For studying the art of debating

____h Extremely small

____i In a hard-hearted way

____j Confused

____k Said easily and smoothly

____l In a cringingly obedient way

____m A witty thought expressed in a few words

____n Odd

____o Sent out, as rays

____p Skinned

____q Fretfully

____r Done without preparation

____s Horrifying or barbaric

____t Highest point

____u With excessive enthusiasm

____v Insanely

____w Not to be broken

____x Tending to prey on other animals

SCORE _____ (Top Score 24)

90

Vocabulary Study/11

If you learn just a few Latin words, you can learn hundreds of English words built from these words. In this lesson ten Latin roots are given. (A root is the base or stem of a word.) The meaning of each root is given. Then two English words built from the root are given with their meanings. Then two more derived words are listed. Write the meaning of each of these words. If you are not sure of a meaning, use your dictionary.

1 **aqua** meaning "water"
aqualung — device for breathing under water

aqueous — watery

aquarium _____

aqueduct _____

2 **corp, corpor** meaning "body"
corporal — of the human body, physical

corpuscle — tiny body forming part of the blood

corporate _____

corpulent _____

3 **domin** meaning "master," "lord"
domain — territory over which one is master

dominion — supreme authority; sovereign power; absolute ownership

dominate _____

domineer _____

4 **mort** meaning "death"
mortal — liable to death

mortification — humiliation

mortally _____

mortician _____

5 **multi** meaning "many," "much"
multiply — increase in number

multigraph — machine for copying typewritten material

multiple _____

multimillionaire _____

6 **omni** meaning "all"
omnibus — bus that carries many people

omnipotent — all powerful

omnipresent _____

omnivorous _____

7 **ped** meaning "foot"
centipede — small, wormlike animal with many pairs of legs

pedestrian — a foot traveler

impede _____

velocipede _____

8 **prim** meaning "first"
prime — of first importance or quality

primitive — first or early in development

primary _____

primate _____

9 **soci** meaning "companion"
social — pertaining to companionship

socialism — system of social organization based on collective ownership

sociable _____

sociology _____

10 **sol** meaning "alone"
sole — being the only one

solitude — state of being alone

soliloquy _____

solitaire _____

SCORE _____ **(Top Score 20)**

Vocabulary Study/12

One meaning of **pro** is "for," and one meaning of **con** is "against." The prefix **pro** can mean "before," "for," "in front," "forth," "in behalf of," "in place of," "according to." The prefix **con** can mean "with," "together," "very." Add the needed letters to make ten **pro** words and ten **con** words. Each blank indicates a letter. The definition follows the blanks. A possible use of the word is indicated in the parentheses.

1 Pro __ __ __ not sacred (_____ literature)

2 Pro __ __ __ __ declare, admit freely (to _____ ignorance)

3 Pro __ __ __ offer for acceptance (to _____ assistance)

4 Pro __ __ __ __ __ __ expert, skilled (a _____ typist)

5 Pro __ __ __ __ side view of the face (not a fullface, but a _____ view)

6 Pro __ __ __ __ __ deep, intense (a _____ thinker, like Einstein)

7 Pro __ __ __ __ offspring (not only for our generation but for our _____)

8 Pro __ __ __ __ __ forbid (laws that _____ gambling)

9 Pro __ __ __ __ __ preface, introduction (the _____ to a play)

10 Pro __ __ __ __ __ __ __ expected, hoped for (a _____ customer)

92

1 Con __ __ __ __ __ __ having a high opinion of oneself (so _____ that one thinks one can do anything)

2 Con __ __ __ __ thought, general idea (Galileo changed our _____ of the solar system.)

3 Con __ __ __ __ __ __ __ that which is yielded (Both sides made a _____ and the treaty was signed.)

4 Con __ __ __ __ condensed, short (a clear, _____ statement)

5 Con __ __ __ __ __ __ blocked, overcrowded (_____ traffic)

6 Con __ __ __ __ __ __ __ a guess (only a _____, unsupported by evidence)

7 Con __ __ __ __ to summon a devil or spirit (to _____ a genie, as Aladdin did)

8 Con __ __ __ __ __ __ __ to make sacred ("We cannot _____, we cannot hallow this ground.")

9 Con __ __ __ __ __ __ __ __ in order, one after the other (It rained on four _____ days.)

10 Con __ __ __ __ __ __ __ catching (a _____ disease, like whopping cough)

SCORE _____ (Top Score 20)

Vocabulary Study/13

An error like "Two people can ride on a tantrum" is called a "boner." A something-like-it word is used for the right word: *tantrum* for *tandem*. In each sentence, cross out the word that is incorrectly used. Write the correct word at the end of the sentence. Be able to give the meaning of both words.

1 The convention would be open to any state declared edible by the United Nations. _____ _____

2 The President discarded most of the prepared talk and spoke extraneously from notes. _____ _____

3 She has a modest, almost self-defacing manner. _____

4 The insurgent in the patient's side was five inches long. _____

5 The flood reports did not tell the extent of the travesty. _____

6 Jane has a real genius for acting; according to her teacher, all she needs is a course in electrocution to finish her off properly. _____

7 The president then introduced Mr. Meeker, who, in his own inimical fashion, served as toastmaster for the evening. _____

8 If you are decapitated due to illness, your salary will be mailed to you. _____

9 Mother thinks I need new glasses, and so she made an appointment for me at the optimist's. _____ _____

10 Gibraltar is considered an invisible fortress. _____

What is the best, or most practical, thing to do with each of these? At the left, write the letter of the answer that most clearly illustrates the meaning of the italicized word.

___ 1 *an anemone?* — (a) put it in the soup, (b) pick it in the woods, (c) ask him his real name, (d) put it back in the cupboard.

___ 2 *a piazza?* — (a) sit out on it, (b) eat it at an Italian restaurant, (c) play a tune on it, (d) exchange it for American money.

___ 3 *a jerkin?* — (a) put it in a relish, (b) train it to wait quietly, (c) tie up a boat at it, (d) wear it.

___ 4 *a malady?* — (a) try to cure it, (b) admire her costume, (c) try to put him at his ease, (d) put him in jail.

___ 5 *a diadem?* — (a) lecture from it, (b) wear it on your finger, (c) put it on your head, (d) deposit it in the bank.

___ 6 *a bolster?* — (a) strain vegetables with it, (b) put a gun in it, (c) put it on the bed, (d) pick cotton with it.

___ 7 *a valise?* — (a) dance it, (b) swallow it, (c) answer it, (d) pack clothes in it.

___ 8 *a vendor?* — (a) open it for more air, (b) buy something from him, (c) scrape it off to see what is underneath, (d) grant him the respect due the aged.

___ 9 *a paddock?* — (a) throw a harpoon at it, (b) put your horse into it, (c) grow rice in it, (d) use it to get your boat moving.

___10 *an auger?* — (a) get over it in time, (b) run away from it as fast as you can, (c) bore holes with it, (d) tell him you don't believe in fortune-telling.

SCORE _____ **(Top Score 20)**

Vocabulary Study/14

On the line at the left write the letter of the word or word group that means the same or nearly the same as the italicized word.

___ 1 *apparition* — (a) complicated machinery, (b) ghostly appearance, (c) soothing application, (d) on-the-job training, (e) room divider

___ 2 *entrepreneur* — (a) slave driver, (b) intimate friend, (c) will-o'-the-wisp, (d) business venturer, (e) talkative person

___ 3 *impeach* — (a) remove from office, (b) deliver a sermon, (c) put a curse on, (d) behave virtuously, (e) accuse of misconduct in office

___ 4 *labyrinth* — (a) workshop, (b) maze, (c) place for bathing, (d) cluster of trees, (e) jeweled necklace

___ 5 *pillage* — (a) plunder, (b) dose of medicine, (c) cushion materials, (d) series of columns, (e) ridicule

___ 6 *promontory* — (a) promise to pay, (b) public walk, (c) forward push, (d) quick action, (e) headland

___ 7 *broach* — (a) close a gap, (b) ask a favor, (c) cook over a flame, (d) mention, (e) trespass

___ 8 *engender* — (a) produce, (b) classify by sex, (c) indicate possession, (d) deduce, (e) deny entrance

___ 9 *engross* — (a) occupy fully, (b) behave very badly, (c) eat too much, (d) enter a complaint, (e) break into parts

___10 *rendezvous* — (a) hotel, (b) emotional disturbance, (c) relinquishment, (d) short poem, (e) meeting place

___11 *salvage* — (a) soothe, (b) save from loss, (c) offer on a platter, (d) rob, (e) add seasoning

___12 *abstinence* — (a) stubbornness, (b) insulting behavior, (c) righteousness, (d) forbearance, (e) nonconformity

___13 *acrid* — (a) dry, (b) covering a considerable territory, (c) sharp to the taste, (d) bright, (e) energetic

___14 *alienate* — (a) sue, (b) deport, (c) estrange, (d) make sick, (e) appease

___15 *carrion* — (a) dead and rotting flesh, (b) soldiers, (c) clear and shrill call, (d) heavy-duty truck, (e) noisy party

___16 *harangue* — (a) large ape, (b) closed carriage, (c) delaying action, (d) pattern of slanting lines, (e) ranting speech

___17 *ferret* — (a) put chains on, (b) carry across a river, (c) deck out, (d) draw out of hiding, (e) grumble

___18 *conciliate* — (a) add to a will, (b) systematize, (c) hurry, (d) pacify, (e) bring to an end

___19 *auspicious* — (a) overbearing, (b) favorable, (c) stern, (d) majestic, (e) overweight

___20 *capitulate* — (a) cut off the head, (b) make fun of, (c) hurl, (d) change one's mind, (e) surrender

94

Vocabulary Study/15

At the left of the number write the letter of the word or phrase that is most nearly **opposite** in meaning to the italicized word.

___ 1 *abomination* — (a) continuation, (b) liking, (c) digestion, (d) aversion, (e) success

___ 2 *bountiful* — (a) pertaining to the land, (b) generous, (c) determined, (d) unlimited, (e) stingy

___ 3 *coy* — (a) reserved, (b) masculine, (c) afraid, (d) intelligent, (e) bold

___ 4 *debase* — (a) cure, (b) begin, (c) raise, (d) make fun of, (e) reduce in value

___ 5 *demure* — (a) impolite, (b) uncomplaining, (c) immodest, (d) inhibited, (e) out of proportion

___ 6 *diffidence* — (a) confidence, (b) shyness, (c) concern, (d) similarity, (e) compactness

___ 7 *disconsolate* — (a) happy, (b) unified, (c) comfortless, (d) harmonious, (e) steady

___ 8 *disheveled* — (a) stored away, (b) clean, (c) encouraged, (d) tidy, (e) ruffled

___ 9 *doff* — (a) greet, (b) trail behind, (c) remain firm, (d) put on, (e) be caught

___10 *dormant* — (a) spineless, (b) untamed, (c) flexible, (d) sleeping, (e) active

___11 *elation* — (a) promptness, (b) high spirits, (c) despair, (d) apparentness, (e) stillness

___12 *embellished* — (a) adorned, (b) thin, (c) poised, (d) plain, (e) stolen

___13 *extricate* — (a) admit, (b) destroy, (c) entangle, (d) overestimate, (e) free

___14 *fealty* — (a) disloyalty, (b) intangible property, (c) insensitivity, (d) lack of skill, (e) obligation

___15 *fictitious* — (a) untruthful, (b) imaginary, (c) literary, (d) genuine, (e) constant

___16 *finesse* — (a) delicacy, (b) cheapness, (c) strength, (d) inattention, (e) clumsiness

___17 *flippant* — (a) permanent, (b) strong, (c) respectful, (d) happy, (e) unsteady

___18 *gainsay* — (a) repeat, (b) affirm, (c) give up, (d) misdirect, (e) deny

___19 *inanimate* — (a) faraway, (b) alive, (c) hard, (d) lifeless, (e) yielding

___20 *indigenous* — (a) wealthy, (b) wandering, (c) natural, (d) pleased, (e) foreign

___21 *indulgent* — (a) strict, (b) humoring, (c) skinny, (d) overweight, (e) sober

___22 *innate* — (a) casual, (b) guilty, (c) native, (d) nervous, (e) acquired

___23 *malign* — (a) pretend, (b) flatter, (c) heal, (d) succeed, (e) slander

___24 *mitigate* — (a) purify, (b) aggravate, (c) lessen, (d) settle out of court, (c) cease fighting

___25 *morose* — (a) sullen, (b) alert, (c) sleepy, (d) cheerful, (e) stupid

SCORE _____ **(Top Score 25)**

Vocabulary Study/16

The first two words form a pair. Find the word that makes a similar pair with the third word. Write the letter of this word at the left.

EXAMPLE: _d_ hatband : hat : : frieze : (a) dress, (b) equator, (c) cake, (d) wall

___ 1 busy : bee : : wily : (a) lion, (b) goose, (c) tiger, (d) fox

___ 2 broccoli : vegetable : : brocade : (a) book, (b) fabric, (c) vehicle, (d) shoe

___ 3 ducks : decoy : : mice : (a) cheese, (b) rodent, (c) family, (d) quietness

___ 4 chair : sitting : : pallet : (a) riding, (b) drinking, (c) sailing, (d) sleeping

___ 5 pecuniary : money : : culinary : (a) kitchen, (b) leather, (c) farm, (d) color

___ 6 spouse : marriage : : accomplice : (a) partner,(b) divorce, (c) crime, (d) war

___ 7 censer : incense : : fireplace : (a) bricks, (b) wood, (c) snake, (d) hearth

___ 8 hypocritical : sincere : : inarticulate : (a) skillful, (b) artistic, (c) distinct, (d) unintelligible

___ 9 tepid : hot : : cool : (a) warm, (b) snowy, (c) blustery, (d) frigid

___10 zephyr : gale : : sprinkle : (a) thunder, (b) downpour, (c) earthquake, (d) umbrella

At the left write the letter of the word that best completes the sentence.

EXAMPLE: _b_ If sewage from the factories is dumped into the river, it will _____ the water. (a) mutilate, (b) contaminate, (c) endue, (d) imbue, (e) pilfer

___ 1 It was later found that an error had been made in the certification, and so the marriage was _____. (a) pronounced, (b) amassed, (c) accelerated, (d) retrieved, (e) annulled

___ 2 The artist grew up on a ranch, and he carries out the Western _____ in all his designs. (a) fanaticism, (b) aesthetic, (c) flavor, (d) motif, (e) spirit

___ 3 The speaker _____ his statement by giving examples and illustrations. (a) distended, (b) precluded, (c) incited, (d) amplified, (e) evoked

___ 4 Since Lois is so good at _____, we'll ask her to draw the cartoons for the "School Personalities" page. (a) caricature, (b) deposition, (c) characterization, (d) intuition, (e) parable

___ 5 Linda is a vibrant, exciting individual, and Bob is completely _____ of her. (a) sated, (b) deluded, (c) cowered, (d) amalgamated, (e) enamored

___ 6 The warships of a country at war may seize and destroy _____ goods which are being shipped to its enemy in neutral ships. (a) flagrant, (b) mercantile, (c) contraband, (d) obnoxious, (e) poisonous

___ 7 Woodchucks, frogs, and snakes _____ during cold weather and hence need no food in the winter. (a) encroach, (b) hibernate, (c) efface, (d) transpire, (e) migrate

___ 8 The Better Business Bureau was organized to protect the public from unfair, misleading, and _____ advertising and business methods. (a) facetious, (b) fraudulent, (c) callous, (d) implacable, (e) ungainly

___ 9 All day long it was talk, talk, talk; I had never before met such a _____ person. (a) voluptuous, (b) vociferous, (c) vivacious, (d) voluble, (e) visionary

___10 The rest of us grew tired and stopped, but John was seemingly _____ and kept on and on. (a) indefatigable, (b) versatile, (c) tenacious, (d) agile, (e) conversant

SCORE _____ (Top Score 20)

Vocabulary Study/17

Here are some common Greek combining forms and their meanings. Each one is numbered. Add the forms, according to the directions, to make good English words. On the line following each "equation," write the English word formed and a short definition of the word.

1 **anthropo** — human being
2 **arch** — ruler
3 **auto** — self
4 **bio** — life
5 **geo** — earth
6 **graph, graphy** — writing
7 **litho, lith** stone

8 **logy** — science of
9 **mega** — large
10 **meter, metry** —measure
11 **micro** — small
12 **mon, mono** — one
13 **patho, path** — suffering
14 **phone** — sound

15 **photo** — light
16 **psycho** — mind
17 **scope** — means for seeing
18 **stat** — apparatus for holding stationary
19 **tele** — far, far away
20 **thermo** — heat

EXAMPLE: $4 + 8 =$ _biology—the science of life_

$1 + 8 =$ _____

$12 + 2 =$ _____

$3 + 6 =$ _____

$4 + 6 =$ _____

$5 + 8 =$ _____

$19 + 6 =$ _____

$7 + 6 =$ _____

$13 + 8 =$ _____

$9 + 14 =$ _____

$11 + 10 =$ _____

$11 + 17 =$ _____

$12 + 7 =$ _____

$16 + 13 =$ _____

$11 + 14 =$ _____

$15 + 10 =$ _____

$16 + 8 =$ _____

$19 + 17 =$ _____

$20 + 18 =$ _____

$19 + 15 =$ _____

$20 + 10 =$ _____

SCORE _____ (Top Score 20)

Vocabulary Study/18

Some words that seem to resemble each other often have completely different meanings. A superficial resemblance between words may cause a person to refer to someone as "the curio of the museum" (*curio* for *curator*). A person who knows the meaning of the words he uses will not make such "boners."

In each of the following sentences cross out the "boner." After the sentence write the word, and the meaning of the word, that should have been used.

1 The forecast says "Northwest winds diminishing a little and rather high humanity."

_____

2 Misinformed shellfish are most likely to grow pearls.

_____

3 The Bureau of Standards insures the use of uninformed weights and measures.

_____

4 The dinner will be held in the Oak Room, and the lecture will be given in the adjourning room.

_____

5 Fortunately, we were able to administer the anecdote and revive them.

_____

6 Anne had an airy feeling as she peered in the window of the haunted house.

_____

7 Most diseases are not inherited; a few are congenial.

_____

8 The judge declared that the testimony was irreverent to the facts.

_____

9 It is rumored that the neglected and dilated house down the street is haunted.

_____

10 These people were very wealthy; they were business typhoons.

_____

11 The two parts of an egg are the albumen and the yoke.

_____

12 It's just a small gift, but it will serve as a memorandum of your visit.

_____

13 Another name for a funeral parlor is a moratorium.

_____

14 The inscription on a tomb is called an epithet.

_____

15 We get our water from artisan wells.

_____

98

SCORE _____ (Top Score 15)

Vocabulary Study/19

The following sentences are taken from magazine articles. Read each sentence and try to figure out the meaning of the italicized word from the context. On the line provided, write what you think the word means. Check your answer with the dictionary.

1 The typhoon-*wracked* China Coast is a rough spot at any time.

_____

2 An unbelievably *oppressive* blanket of humidity lies over the area, and perspiration clings to the suffocating skin like acid.

_____

3 On nights when the foghorn bellows and the surf thunders on the rocks, the lighthouse keepers sleep *fitfully*.

_____

4 Mr. Busch admitted frankly that he had never been an ardent *devotee* of the national pastime of baseball.

_____

5 I'm fairly *fluent*, and usually I have no trouble starting a conversation.

_____

6 In dry spells cowhands, using special blowtorches, *singe* the prickly pears to remove their spines, and the juicy leaves make good roughage for cattle.

_____

7 You can't blame the President for a drought; it's silly to try to make him the *scapegoat* of the disaster.

_____

8 The Romans adored oysters; Vitellius, a notoriously *gluttonous* emperor, is credited with having consumed more oysters at a single sitting than any other man—well over a thousand.

_____

9 As a result of her *festering* wound, Caroline was advised by her doctors to remain at University Hospital an extra two weeks.

_____

10 In this desert the hollows between the mesquite-covered *hummocks* are sprinkled with fragments of brilliantly painted pottery.

_____

11 Contrary to *fallacious* public opinion, a jet engine does not push against the air to gain its impetus.

_____

12 Oysters are the most *sedentary* creatures imaginable; having no means of locomotion, they attach themselves in infancy to whatever hard surface they happen to settle on.

_____

13 For some reason, many people refuse to taste catfish, but I think it's one of the most *succulent* of table fish.

_____

14 On game nights the gymnasium is a complete *bedlam* with a brass band trying to break out the walls and a few hundred shrill voices added to the din.

_____

SCORE _____ (Top Score 14)

Vocabulary Study/20

This vocabulary lesson is devoted to words pertaining to business. New and young employees cannot be expected to have the specialized knowledge that experienced people have, but they should have a general knowledge of commonly used business terms.

After reading each sentence, underline the words or phrases which most nearly fit the meaning of the italicized words as used in the sentence. You may need to refer to the dictionary.

EXAMPLE: Since he had sufficient collateral, you will be reimbursed for the loan.

collateral — business sense, side interest, <u>property offered as security</u>, money in the bank

reimbursed — pleased, <u>repaid</u>, granted an interview, notified

1 Ms. Olin requires her salespeople to render a strict accounting of all their expenditures.

accounting — savings, alibi, record, complaint

expenditures — extravagances, spending, investments, losses

2 If we are to avoid bankruptcy, we must obtain capital to finance our operations until we can fill our backlog.

bankruptcy — holding up a bank, insolvency, interruption of business, loss of prestige

capital — influence, money, punishment, debts

finance — pay for, liquidate, ship, sell

operations — surgery, military actions, work, gambling

backlog — bank account, unfilled orders, deficit, warehouse

3 The union, which is an affiliate of the American Federation of Labor, is negotiating with the management of Glee & Co., a subsidiary of Thornton, Inc.

union — the United States, radicals, consolidation, labor organization

affiliate — associate, enemy, competitor, supporter

negotiating — bickering, cheating, seeking to come to terms, getting angry

management — competitor, executives, subordinates, foremen

subsidiary — submarine manufacturer, successor, firm controlled by another, dairy concern

Inc. — legal corporation, ink factory, incapacitated or bankrupt firm, bank

4 The accrued interest on your debentures now exceeds the principal.

accrued — accumulated, forfeited, compound, simple

interest — excitement, debt, right, capital earnings

debentures — certificates of indebtedness, bills, bent products, factories

principal — school official, profit, capital sum, loss

5 The corporation's franchise expires at the end of this fiscal year.

corporation — farmers' cooperative, factory, retail store, group recognized as a legal entity

franchise — permit to trade with France, permit to do business, right to vote, right to send letters without postage

fiscal — current, favorable, September 1 to August 31, pertaining to the period for which accounts are balanced

100

Vocabulary Study/21

This vocabulary lesson and Vocabulary Study 22 are modeled upon the verbal-aptitude sections of college-entrance examinations. Each of the lessons is different, for different types of questions appear in college-entrance examinations. Be sure to read the directions carefully.

On the line at the left of the number, write the letter of the word or word group that means the same or nearly the same as the italicized word.

—— 1 *denizen* — (a) evil spirit, (b) fish, (c) traveler, (d) society woman, (e) inhabitant

—— 2 *suppliant* — (a) diner, (b) addition, (c) dancer, (d) theory, (e) petitioner

—— 3 *tenure* — (a) suspense, (b) decade, (c) experiment, (d) holding, (e) force

—— 4 *longevity* — (a) foresight, (b) great distance, (c) practical joke, (d) length of life, (e) patience

—— 5 *incumbent* — (a) obligatory, (b) newly arrived, (c) out of shape, (d) poor, (e) ineffectual

—— 6 *ruminate* — (a) search, (b) vomit, (c) ponder, (d) dream, (e) wander

—— 7 *reticent* — (a) late, (b) silent, (c) held back, (d) following, (e) well-behaved

—— 8 *rampant* — (a) excited, (b) irritated, (c) unrestrained, (d) haphazard, (e) protected

—— 9 *vagary* — (a) caprice, (b) indefiniteness, (c) beggar, (d) excessive pride, (e) emptiness

——10 *acme* — (a) skin condition, (b) envy, (c) center, (d) highest point, (e) prized possession

——11 *stoic* — (a) heroic, (b) unfathomable, (c) stupid, (d) thick, (e) impassive

——12 *parley* — (a) bet, (b) front room, (c) conference, (d) standard, (e) barrage

——13 *subjugate* — (a) join, (b) conquer, (c) judge, (d) elevate, (e) expose

——14 *verity* — (a) change, (b) truth, (c) eternity, (d) short poem, (e) unusual excellence

——15 *presage* — (a) publish, (b) apply pressure, (c) make ready, (d) keep safe, (e) portend

——16 *obviate* — (a) atone for, (b) make unnecessary, (c) die, (d) invalidate, (e) forget

——17 *elicit* — (a) break a law, (b) escape, (c) omit, (d) give permission, (e) draw out

——18 *enigma* — (a) itching, (b) fatigue, (c) boredom, (d) puzzle, (e) beauty

——19 *abrogate* — (a) annul, (b) introduce, (c) irritate, (d) forgive, (e) condense

——20 *condone* — (a) pardon, (b) sympathize, (c) entrust, (d) disapprove, (e) argue

——21 *criterion* — (a) estimate, (b) illegal agreement, (c) standard, (d) religious principle, (e) sampling

——22 *florid* — (a) intoxicated, (b) strange, (c) high-colored, (d) tropical, (e) ill

——23 *foible* — (a) ornament, (b) failing, (c) trick, (d) sin, (e) burden

——24 *ebullient* — (a) bubbly, (b) receding, (c) stubborn, (d) wealthy, (e) threatening

——25 *cursory* — (a) superficial, (b) matter-of-fact, (c) thorough, (d) censorious, (e) out-of-the-way

SCORE _____ (Top Score 25)

Vocabulary Study/22

On the line at the left of the number, write the letter of the word that is most nearly opposite in meaning to the italicized word.

___ 1 *convene* — (a) meet, (b) hamper, (c) disband, (d) release, (e) accommodate

___ 2 *diffusion* — (a) dimness, (b) dispersal, (c) similarity, (d) order, (e) concentration

___ 3 *dolorous* — (a) poor, (b) wide-awake, (c) anguished, (d) joyful, (e) masculine

___ 4 *emaciated* — (a) unemotional, (b) fat, (c) unsympathetic, (d) fleshless, (e) fragrant

___ 5 *fusion* — (a) coalescence, (b) bombardment, (c) carelessness, (d) vagueness, (e) separation

___ 6 *spurious* — (a) impulsive, (b) genuine, (c) false, (d) thoughtful, (e) complimentary

___ 7 *jeopardy* — (a) trust, (b) vulnerability, (c) reprieve, (d) safety, (e) victory

___ 8 *reprimand* — (a) payment, (b) attraction, (c) commendation, (d) reproof, (e) self-esteem

___ 9 *proximity* — (a) remoteness, (b) absence, (c) repulsion, (d) extravagance, (e) nearness

___10 *perfunctory* — (a) indifferent, (b) fresh, (c) unofficial, (d) zealous, (e) servile

___11 *pretentious* — (a) real, (b) showy, (c) modest, (d) imaginary, (e) portentous

___12 *satiate* — (a) please, (b) lighten, (c) surfeit (d) starve, (e) dehydrate

___13 *unwonted* — (a) customary, (b) desired, (c) heralded, (d) deserved, (e) unexpected

___14 *vacillation* — (a) steadiness, (b) occupation, (c) shamelessness, (d) hesitation, (e) health

___15 *penury* — (a) stinginess, (b) affability, (c) employment, (d) thoughtfulness, (e) opulence

___16 *abortive* — (a) exact, (b) fruitless, (c) successful, (d) deterring, (e) enjoyable

___17 *contrite* — (a) unforgiving, (b) ingenuous, (c) sorry, (d) flattering, (e) impenitent

___18 *alleviate* — (a) make sad, (b) unite, (c) aggravate, (d) raise, (e) relieve

___19 *altruistic* — (a) selfish, (b) untrustworthy, (c) incompetent, (d) egoistic, (e) unchanged

___20 *egress* — (a) emergence, (b) fame, (c) baldness, (d) shield, (e) entrance

___21 *ameliorate* — (a) sweeten, (b) worsen, (c) improve, (d) resist change, (e) forget

___22 *innocuous* — (a) consequential, (b) harmful, (c) vaccinated, (d) guilty, (e) noninjurious

___23 *astute* — (a) crooked, (b) stupid, (c) thin, (d) sagacious, (e) full-grown

___24 *clemency* — (a) depression, (b) mercy, (c) difficulty, (d) harshness, (e) cheerfulness

___25 *ephemeral* — (a) long-lived, (b) grave, (c) rugged, (d) bony, (e) fleeting

SCORE _____ **(Top Score 25)**

Sentence Completeness

I. *Sentence Sense*   15 Points

On the line preceding each group of words, write **0** if the group is not a complete sentence; write **1** if the group is one complete sentence; or write **2** if the group is two sentences incorrectly written as one.

EXAMPLE: __0__ A wonderful place for a picnic.

___ 1 Bring your camera with you when you come to see me.

___ 2 When all the arrangements were made for a celebration.

___ 3 Wandering along a lonely country road in the hot sun.

___ 4 Enrique is the most energetic student in our class, he never seems to be tired.

___ 5 Saw a wonderful television program last Sunday.

___ 6 Striving always to do good work, Donna reached her goal.

___ 7 Reading is pleasant entertainment what kind of reading do you like?

___ 8 After the excitement of the day was finally over.

___ 9 Bob Weldon is class president all the members respect him greatly.

___10 A beautiful valley surrounded by rugged mountains.

___11 It was the most exciting game of the season we won by two points.

___12 Just the kind of afternoon for a tennis match.

___13 The principal and the teachers called the meeting and made the plans.

___14 While Helen and I waited for the other golfers.

___15 Because he was always impatient with other people.

Plain English Handbook, 1–4, 33–37.

II. *Essential Parts of the Sentence*   20 Points

For each sentence, write the simple subject on the first line and the simple predicate on the second line.

EXAMPLE: _____*Longfellow*_____ _____*Was born*_____ Was Longfellow born in Maine?

_____ _____ 1 Has our club constitution been written?

_____ _____ 2 After days of rain came the sunshine.

_____ _____ 3 The dog, expecting its master, had been waiting a long time.

_____ _____ 4 Has Marcella returned from Boston?

_____ _____ 5 Above the highest peak floated a big cloud.

_____ _____ 6 Sleeping quietly, the dog did not see us.

_____ _____ 7 Around the mill were blooming many flowers.

_____ _____ 8 Was Joe, our club chairperson, at the game?

_____ _____ 9 Have the boys been walking to school?

_____ _____ 10 Behind the parade rode Ed on a big horse.

Plain English Handbook, 3, 4, 13, 15.

III. *Combining Groups of Words* 65 Points

Make one complete sentence of the two groups of words in each item by indicating the punctuation and capitalization needed at each point marked by a number in parentheses. Tell the part of speech of the italicized words. On the first line (marked 1) before each item give the class of the reconstructed sentence. Use the following key:

S — simple	a — comma	d — no punctuation	g — pronoun	j — adverb
Cd — compound	b — semicolon	e — small letter	h — verb	k — adjective
Cx — complex	c — colon	f — conjunction	i — noun	l — preposition

EXAMPLE: 1 _S_ 2 _a_ 3 _e_ 4 _k_ We enjoyed the show[2] [3]Especially the [4]*musical* numbers.

1 _ 2 _ 3 _ 4 _ 1 Juan cannot win the contest [2] [3]Unless he [4]*works* harder.

1 _ 2 _ 3 _ 4 _ 5 _ 2 Al is always courteous [2] [3]He [4]is a [5]*thoughtful* person.

1 _ 2 _ 3 _ 4 _ 3 Alice is [2]*chairperson* of the group[3] [4]She is a sophomore.

1 _ 2 _ 3 _ 4 _ 5 _ 4 Jo is [2]*extremely* ambitious[3] [4]She always uses good [5]*language*.

1 _ 2 _ 3 _ 4 _ 5 Ted dreams of a great [2]*future*[3] [4]But dreams cannot bring success.

1 _ 2 _ 3 _ 4 _ 5 _ 6 Before the others came[2] [3]He and I had[4]*the* [5]*work* done.

1 _ 2 _ 3 _ 4 _ 7 Success requires work[2] [3]But some people [4]*shun* hard work.

1 _ 2 _ 3 _ 4 _ 5 _ 8 Dot and Stu [2]*wrote* the stories[3] Liz [4]*and* [5]I edited them.

1 _ 2 _ 3 _ 4 _ 9 Maria wrote her story[2] [3]Before [4]*she* came to school.

1 _ 2 _ 3 _ 4 _ 10 Jack is very careless[2] [3]He will [4]*never* finish in time.

1 _ 2 _ 3 _ 4 _ 11 Many people enjoy sports[2] [3]Particularly [4]*football*.

1 _ 2 _ 3 _ 4 _ 12 Mr. Hitt worked for years[2] [3]Hoping to reach his [4]*goal*.

1 _ 2 _ 3 _ 4 _ 5 _ 13 Ed [2]*usually* does [3]*good* work[4] [5]Surely he is a strong candidate.

1 _ 2 _ 3 _ 4 _ 14 Surmounting [2]*great* difficulties[3] [4]She became a success.

1 _ 2 _ 3 _ 4 _ 15 Kay wanted to help[2] [3]However [4]*she* had homework.

Plain English Handbook, 20–23, 31–45, 52, 490, 495, 497, 499.

SCORE _____ (Top Score 100)

UNIT II

Verbs
INVENTORY 2

I. *Transitive and Intransitive Verbs* Points

If the verb in the sentence is transitive, write **vt** before the sentence. If it is intransitive, write **vi.**

EXAMPLE: _vt_ Have those girls been invited to the party?

___ 1 Did Fred help the girls with the program last week?

___ 2 Alice and Roger had been gathering tomatoes from the garden.

___ 3 Did you see Henry and George at the meeting last night?

___ 4 The sailplane soared gracefully above the hills.

___ 5 Have the others gone to the soccer match?

___ 6 Have all the tickets been sold so early in the day?

___ 7 Jan should have written those invitations yesterday.

___ 8 Dinner tasted good after our long walk to camp.

___ 9 Those other boys should have been helping Tom and me.

___10 Marie might have brought these pictures to us.

Plain English Handbook, 173–178, 180, 212, 213.

II. *Tenses of Verbs* Points

Before each sentence write the correct tense form of the verb in parentheses.

EXAMPLE: _____*had seen*_____ Elaine and I (**see** — past perfect) that famous picture before.

_____ 1 The children (**eat** — past) the candy that we gave them.

_____ 2 The younger boys (**swim** — past) until they were exhausted.

_____ 3 Dave (**go** — present perfect) to New Orleans with his family.

_____ 4 The kittens often (**lie** — present) in front of the fire.

_____ 5 The sun (**rise** — past) before we had finished breakfast.

_____ 6 Hal (**write** — past perfect) his assigned theme before school began.

_____ 7 Bob (**come** — past perfect) before we left the party.

_____ 8 Our music teacher (**give** — present perfect) us these concert tickets.

_____ 9 Beth and she (**do** — past) their very best to win.

_____10 My jacket (**lie** — past perfect) on the ground all night.

_____11 The stonemasons (**lay** — past perfect) heavy stones on the wall.

_____12 Tom and Ken (**sit** — past) there until Bob returned.

_____13 We (**know** — present perfect) Gary ever since he started school.

_____14 Larry surely (**run** — past perfect) a good race at the meet.

_____15 Pat (**take** — present perfect) her report to class.

Plain English Handbook, 190–196, 204, 207, 216, 217.

III. *Using Verbs*

25 Points

Correct each incorrect verb form by writing the correct form on the line before the sentence. There may be more than one incorrect verb in some sentences. If there is no incorrect verb, write **C**. It may help you to cross out the incorrect word.

EXAMPLE: _____*Were*_____ ~~Was~~ Helen and her cousin here when you came?

_____ 1 There goes Nan and Jean, and the others have already went.   (239, 204)

_____ 2 Mrs. Scott is one of those managers who is always ready to listen.   (241)

_____ 3 Neither Kay nor her roommates were present when Don and he came.   (238, 204)

_____ 4 Bill and I laid down on the ground and rested.   (217)

_____ 5 Max had ran a good race although the number of contestants were large.   (204, 244)

_____ 6 The coach gave us full instructions before the game began.   (204)

_____ 7 After I came into the room, he raised to his feet.   (204, 216, 217)

_____ 8 Either Jo or the boys was to stay after the others had gone.   (238, 204)

_____ 9 Jed did well in the game, but you was the real star.   (216, 260)

_____10 We had already began work when Tim came.   (204, 216)

_____11 Neither the girls nor Ted think it is me who sent the letter.   (238, 180)

_____12 Ben does not know which one of the messengers have gone to get Al.   (246)

_____13 I think there was five of us who come in late.   (239, 204)

_____14 If Bob was chairperson, he'd not do as others have did.   (256, 204)

_____15 Joan was here when Leo left, but she don't know where he is.   (197)

_____16 Have Freda and he gave the money to you?   (216)

_____17 The cat came into the room and laid down beside Kathy.   (204, 217)

_____18 Mr. Carman, as well as his friends, liked what we done.   (236, 204)

_____19 Is Bill and Joe ready to go, now that their work is done?   (247, 216)

_____20 When we won the game, our team was given individual awards.   (240)

106

Substantives, Modifiers, and Connectives

I. *Using Substantives*   30 Points

Correct each incorrect noun or pronoun by writing the correct form on the line before the sentence. It may help you to cross out the incorrect word.

EXAMPLE: _____*she*_____ Are you sure it was ~~her~~ who came with Beth and him?   (152, 153)

_____ 1 It was her who made the schedules for us students.   (152, 157)

_____ 2 Joan and him are the two who are to go with Bob and me.   (149, 153)

_____ 3 She is a teacher whom you will find always helps us students.   (159, 157)

_____ 4 Is it him who is to go with Tom and me?   (152, 153)

_____ 5 It was Dick and she whom she asked to help we beginners.   (152, 160, 157)

_____ 6 He and I think that every girl will do their best to win.   (149, 164)

_____ 7 It was Jim and he whom we saw with Jill and she.   (149, 160, 153)

_____ 8 Mr. Webb sent Tom and I the tickets for us students.   (154, 157)

_____ 9 All us members should help our club to keep its lead.   (151, 165)

_____10 Ed and he have the new caps for all us boys but Bo and he.   (149, 157, 156)

_____11 Dick and he act much younger than Sue and her.   (149, 148)

_____12 Could it have been her who sent the books for Ruth and me?   (152, 153)

_____13 It must be Bob and he who work in the mens' shop.   (152, 159, 122)

_____14 Every man should send their ideas to Don or me.   (164, 153)

_____15 It was Todd and she who saw Pat and he at the boat show.   (152, 159, 153)

_____16 Here come Dad and she to go with we friends to the show.   (149, 157)

_____17 Do Kenny and he have the invitations for we girls?   (149, 157)

_____18 It was Bess who came in my father's-in-law car.   (159, 123)

_____19 Leo and he think that Beth and her will invite us boys.   (149, 157)

_____20 Mrs. Hill helped the club to write their constitution.   (165)

_____21 Was it Joe and him who sent the record to Nita and me?   (152, 153)

_____22 She is one whom we think is a friend to all us students.   (159, 157)

_____23 All we girls but Tina and she were at the rally.   (151, 156)

_____24 It wasn't she who brought we boys the bad news.   (152, 155)

_____25 Most of we ushers think it was Sal with Kay and her.   (157, 153)

_____26 No, it wasn't him whom you met with Dan and her.   (152, 160, 153)

_____27 Did the glee club have its robes cleaned?   (165)

_____28 Who do you think sent Betsy and I that funny card?   (159, 154)

_____29 Tom and I think that the students should give they're opinion.   (149, 146)

_____30 It is she whom we think should help Dave with the program.   (152, 159)

II. *Modifiers and Connectives*   20 Points

Correct each incorrect adjective, adverb, preposition, or conjunction by writing the correct form on the line before the sentence. It may help you to cross out the incorrect word.

fewer

EXAMPLE: _____ We students certainly make less mistakes in English now.   (306)

_____ 1 Ted can't win except he does his footwork more carefully.   (370, 311)

_____ 2 He is the older of the two and he sure skates well.   (296, 311, 329)

_____ 3 Kay swims well, but Lou is the best swimmer of the two.   (329, 296)

_____ 4 Anna looked confidently and she surely danced well.   (289, 329)

_____ 5 Joe was really upset because he could not find his hat anywheres.   (311, 330)

_____ 6 Fred is not nearly so tall as Herb, but he is the heaviest of the two.   (310, 296)

_____ 7 Jo was somewhat upset, but she read her part good.   (334, 329)

_____ 8 The book fell in back of the desk as I came into the room.   (363, 357)

_____ 9 I don't feel bad because Henry differs from me in my views.   (289, 360)

_____10 There is surely not no reason for her going with them.   (311, 336)

_____11 Your pen is different than mine, but it is the better of the two.   (337, 296)

_____12 Hank is real intelligent, but he does his work carelessly.   (311)

_____13 Tim is the better athlete of the two, but he should have played different.   (296, 311)

_____14 These cakes are different than those, but they do look good.   (337, 289)

_____15 The river looked beautiful but it smelled badly.   (289)

_____16 Al is some taller than we, and he is the oldest of the four.   (334, 295)

_____17 She behaved so rudely that there wasn't no one to defend her.   (311, 336)

_____18 Did you read where it was to get somewhat colder?   (380, 334)

_____19 He worked carefully and finished the job inside of an hour.   (311, 356)

_____20 Dick surely played well, but he feels badly about losing.   (311, 329, 289)

108

Sentence Structure

I. Sentence Parts   20 Points

Indicate whether the italicized group of words in each sentence is a phrase or a clause by writing **P** or **C** on the first line. On the second line, rewrite the italicized group of words, changing each phrase to a clause and each clause to a phrase.

EXAMPLE: ___C___ _____*Waiting for John,*_____ _____ *While I waited for John,* I washed the dishes.

— _____ 1 Bess, *hoping to be an artist,* is studying painting.

— _____ 2 The guest of honor is the man *who is standing next to Ms. Webb.*

— _____ 3 *As we drove down the turnpike,* we saw many antique cars.

— _____ 4 The girl *wearing blue shorts* is my sister.

— _____ 5 Ellen hopes *that she may go to Africa someday.*

— _____ 6 *Scrambling over the fence,* she saw the bull bearing down on her.

— _____ 7 *After I finished my studies,* I fell into bed.

— _____ 8 *Running to catch the bus,* Jim fell and turned his ankle.

— _____ 9 *As we stood on the beach,* we saw the *China Clipper* come into port.

— _____ 10 I admire people *with a sense of humor.*

Plain English Handbook, 387–409, 422.

II. Sentence Effectiveness   10 Points

Each item consists of two expressions of the same thought. On the line before the sentence number, write **A** or **B** to indicate which is the better sentence.

EXAMPLE: ___B___ **A** The juniors are working diligently. Hoping to sell all the tickets.
    B The juniors, hoping to sell all the tickets, are working diligently.

— 1 **A** By working early and late, the painters finished the job on time.
    B By working early and late, the job was completed on time.

— 2 **A** Jim said, "Bob, we've appointed you chairperson."
    B Jim told Bob that he had been appointed chairperson.

— 3 **A** Calvin Davis is our star athlete, and he jogs to school every morning.
    B Calvin Davis, our star athlete, jogs to school every morning.

— 4 **A** While we were in mountain country, many pine forests were seen.
    B While we were in mountain country, we saw many pine forests.

— 5 **A** James enjoys team sports. Particularly football and basketball.
    B James enjoys team sports, particularly football and basketball.

— 6 **A** Looking far out to sea, we saw many ships.

    B Looking far out to sea, many ships were seen.

— 7 **A** Everyone was happy. When we won the plaque.

    B Everyone was happy when we won the plaque.

— 8 **A** In one of the shops Kay saw a hat which she liked.

    B Kay saw a hat in one of the shops which she liked.

— 9 **A** When we were at the beach, we spent much time swimming.

    B When we were at the beach, much time was spent swimming.

—10 **A** Alice studies music seriously because she hopes to become a conductor.

    B Alice studies music seriously. Because she hopes to become a conductor.

Plain English Handbook, 433, 434, 436, 438, 439, 446, 447, 452, 455.

III. *Words in the Sentence*   20 Points

Correct each incorrectly used word by writing the correct form on the line before the sentence. If there is no incorrect word, write **C** before the sentence.

EXAMPLE: _____*ought*_____ He ~~had ought~~ to drive slower in the city. (225)

_____ 1 Eileen surely looked nervous, but she talked good. (311, 289, 329)

_____ 2 When Hugh and I came, neither Sue nor Clare were here. (149, 204, 237)

_____ 3 As I sat down, he rose to his feet and began to talk. (204, 217)

_____ 4 There are some of us boys who think that you was wrong. (239, 157, 260)

_____ 5 It might of been Pepe whom you saw with her. (230, 160)

_____ 6 Are Faye and she the girls whom you think will go too? (149, 159)

_____ 7 The principal would not leave us sell the tickets. (227)

_____ 8 Your outline is different than mine, but it is the better one. (337, 296)

_____ 9 Either Ms. Howe or the secretaries is to make out the schedule. (238)

_____10 There goes Mrs. DelRosa and the stage crew to set the stage for us dancers. (239, 217, 157)

_____11 Each one of the teachers think that he is the chairperson. (242)

_____12 We had ought to invite Lynn to our party. (225)

_____13 If I were she, I'd ask Tonio why he don't join us. (256, 152, 197)

_____14 Was it Ruth and he who you saw with Bill and her? (152, 160, 153)

_____15 Gail and she have invited we boys to the party. (149, 155)

_____16 Was it Maria who sent the books to Juan and me? (153)

_____17 There wasn't no one here when I came. (239, 336, 204)

_____18 While Don was here, he gathered six basketsful of apples. (87)

_____19 She makes less errors in math than her cousin. (306, 148)

_____20 Ben or they are to come inside of an hour. (238, 356)

SCORE _____ **(Top Score 50)**

Composition and the Use of Words

I. *Paragraphs, Outlines, and Letters*　　　　　　　　　　　15 Points

On the line at the left write the number of the bold-faced word or expression that makes the statement true.

EXAMPLE:　_1_　End punctuation in the heading is ¹not required/²required.　(593)

___ 1 The sentences of a paragraph are ¹loosely/²closely related in thought.　(541)

___ 2 In dialogue each speech is ¹set off by dashes/²separately paragraphed.　(542)

___ 3 The topic sentence is placed ¹first/²anywhere in the paragraph.　(544)

___ 4 Proper arrangement of sentences in a paragraph is called ¹unity/²coherence.　(549)

___ 5 Sticking to the subject in a paragraph is ¹unity/²emphasis.　(548)

___ 6 Topics of an outline should be arranged in ¹just any/²logical order.　(578)

___ 7 The business letter has ¹five/²six parts.　(590)

___ 8 Careful writers use ¹few/²many abbreviations in letters.　(591)

___ 9 The ¹first/²last item of the heading is the date.　(592)

___10 If a salutation consists of *dear* preceded by *my*, ¹both words are capitalized/²only the first word is capitalized.　(595)

___11 A ¹colon/²comma is placed after the salutation of a business letter.　(597)

___12 The participial closing is ¹little/²much used by careful writers.　(599)

___13 In the complimentary close ¹each/²only the first word is capitalized.　(599)

___14 The signature should be followed by ¹no punctuation/²a period.　(600)

___15 A ¹comma/²dash should follow the salutation of a friendly letter.　(617)

II. *Faulty Expressions in the Sentence*　　　　　　　　　　　10 Points

On the line at the left write the number of the bold-faced expression that is correct or more appropriate.

EXAMPLE:　_2_　Almost all the officers ¹suspicioned/²suspected the stranger of the theft.

___ 1 Both of the gentlemen were dressed ¹formerly/²formally.

___ 2 It is ¹strange/²funny that you didn't see the car in time to stop.

___ 3 Those stragglers have only a short ¹ways/²way to go now.

___ 4 The volunteers worked very hard in ¹setting up/²arranging the party.

___ 5 He was ¹angry/²mad because I would go no further with the plans he presented.

___ 6 You ¹had ought to/²ought to do your schoolwork before you go.

___ 7 I think it would be ¹all right/²alright to lend Joan's book to Jack.

___ 8 You will be ¹rather/²kind of tired by the end of a full day of hiking.

___ 9 The change in temperature is ¹likely/²liable to help the spring wheat crop.

___10 How can we ¹teach/²learn them to be more careful?

Plain English Handbook, 665–674.

III. *Using Words in the Sentence*

On the line at the left write the number of the bold-faced word that is the correct form to use in the sentence.

EXAMPLE: _2_ We should trade at ¹Wall's/²Wall and Hill's Store. (124)

___ 1 The members, not the president, ¹is/²are making the arrangements. (261)

___ 2 The cakes didn't look good, but they tasted very ¹good/²well. (289, 312)

___ 3 Neither their language nor their customs are different ¹than/²from ours. (337)

___ 4 Jack is one of those people who ¹is/²are always friendly. (241)

___ 5 Tom and he picked ten ¹basketfuls/²basketsful of apples. (87)

___ 6 Were you here when she told about ¹Tom/²Tom's winning the race? (127)

___ 7 They ¹swum/²swam to shore after their canoe sank. (204)

___ 8 We ¹gave/²give the message to her as soon as we saw her. (204, 216)

___ 9 I am sure that Sandra will go with Marie and ¹she/²her. (153)

___10 Is it she ¹who/²whom you asked to help with the decorations? (160)

___11 If I were he, I'd ¹set/²sit there and wait. (204, 217)

___12 When Dick and I ¹came/²come, you were not here. (204, 216)

___13 He feels ¹bad/²badly because Joe is angry with him. (289, 312)

___14 One of the identical twins stood ¹behind/²in back of the other's desk. (363)

___15 There ¹go/²goes Alicia and Mary with Chico and him. (239)

___16 He may not feel ¹that/²as he can do as we suggest. (379)

___17 She cannot do ¹differently/²different unless we tell her. (311)

___18 John will not finish ¹except/²unless we help him. (370)

___19 Send ¹whomever/²whoever will assist Grace and him. (161)

___20 Neither Jack ¹or/²nor Julio will sell his bicycle. (378)

___21 ¹Was/²Were Bill and Ruth with Ann and him? (247)

___22 The author ¹doesn't/²don't explain how the thieves were caught. (197)

___23 We ¹ate/²eat our breakfast long before the sun rose. (204)

___24 Jack and ¹he/²him must have gone on without you two. (149)

___25 It might have been they who brought ¹we/²us officers the tickets. (155)

SCORE _____ (Top Score 50)

112

Final Inventory/A

I. *Sentence Sense*   10 Points

On the line preceding each group of words, write **0** if the group is not a complete sentence; write **1** if the group is one complete sentence; or write **2** if the group is two sentences incorrectly written as one.

EXAMPLE: **0**   Sitting at the tables in the study hall.

— 1 Cheering wildly, we watched Hex make a touchdown.

— 2 Working, planning, and hoping that a college education would be possible.

— 3 Bring your new tennis racket to school tomorrow.

— 4 Because she had worked so long and so faithfully at perfecting her butterfly stroke.

— 5 It was the most thrilling game of the season our team played well.

— 6 Although the work was difficult, Bill completed the job on time.

— 7 Went fishing with Henry and Joe last Saturday.

— 8 We will meet again on Wednesday, Jorge Gómez will preside.

— 9 When will the performance begin?

—10 While we waited impatiently for the big game to begin.

Plain English Handbook, 1–4, 33–37.

II. *Classifying Sentences and Parts of Speech*   30 Points

On the first line preceding each sentence, indicate its class by writing **S** for simple, **Cd** for compound, or **Cx** for complex. On the next two lines indicate the part of speech of each of the two italicized words by writing **n** for noun, **pron** for pronoun, **adj** for adjective, **adv** for adverb, **v** for verb, **prep** for preposition, or **conj** for conjunction. Class the conjunctive adverb as a conjunction.

EXAMPLE: *Cx pron conj*   *She* came *before* we left the meeting.

— —— —— 1 We played a fast game, *but* we did *not* win.

— —— —— 2 *Harry* wrote and *directed* the school play.

— —— —— 3 *These* perennial plants that you gave me *need* watering.

— —— —— 4 All the lifeguards have gone *but* Hal *and* Glenda.

— —— —— 5 The others are here somewhere, *but* I have not seen *them*.

— —— —— 6 Mary looked *thrilled*, and she performed her part *well*.

— —— —— 7 Working *at* his job, Joe did not see *us* come in.

— —— —— 8 Do you *ever* have trouble with your *pronouns*?

— —— —— 9 *This* is the rock record that Bob *gave* me.

— —— ——10 He does all his *work* well; *therefore*, he surely will succeed.

Plain English Handbook, 20–23, 38–45, 52, 138–140, 320.

III. Substantives and Verbs

Each sentence has three incorrect words. Correct each incorrect noun, pronoun, or verb by writing the correct forms (in their right order) on the lines before the sentence.

he   *were*   *sitting*

_____ _____ _____ **EXAMPLE:** Sue and ~~him was setting~~ on the porch. (149, 247, 204)

_____ _____ _____ 1 The band has ordered its instruments from the shopkeeper who you suggested. (240, 165, 160)

_____ _____ _____ 2 It is him who will bring the visitor and she to they. (96, 160, 153, 106)

_____ _____ _____ 3 It was him and I who saw the oxes and the gooses. (149, 160, 85, 84)

_____ _____ _____ 4 The number of frozen turkies sold by Bell's and Hill's Market have decreased. (81, 124, 244)

_____ _____ _____ 5 Mr. Lee is one of the coaches who is learning we teammates some new plays. (241, 227, 155)

_____ _____ _____ 6 Neither our fathers nor him are able to attend the clubs' meeting. (149, 238, 120)

_____ _____ _____ 7 Bill catched the ball and run for his' first touchdown. (204, 146)

_____ _____ _____ 8 My brother-in-laws and I dug six bushel of potatos. (86, 300, 78)

_____ _____ _____ 9 Neither Pat nor Jan were ready to give their report of what she had did. (237, 142, 164, 204, 216)

_____ _____ _____ 10 All us actors, as well as the director, knows that Paula acts better than him. (151, 236, 148)

_____ _____ _____ 11 The trioes, made up of husbands and wifes, should of sung at the P.T.A. dinner. (79, 82, 230)

_____ _____ _____ 12 The children were setting on the ground while Joe and me laid on the porch. (217, 149)

_____ _____ _____ 13 John thought she to be I. I am often thought to be her. (272, 273, 274)

_____ _____ _____ 14 You was the only one who laughed as if you was amused by the clowns antics. (260, 258, 120)

_____ _____ _____ 15 The farmer sold she and I two bucketsful of blueberries. (154, 87)

_____ _____ _____ 16 Four hundred dollars were paid for his father's-in-law share of the sheeps. (245, 123, 89)

_____ _____ _____ 17 Whom did you say would direct the sophomore girl's and boy's games? (159, 121)

_____ _____ _____ 18 Doesn't Marta and him think they had ought to come tomorrow? (197, 149, 225)

_____ _____ _____ 19 Everyone but Hank and I were surprised at Mary winning the prize. (156, 242, 270)

_____ _____ _____ 20 Alice and Jim's hands was stained by the berrys. (125, 197, 80)

IV. Modifiers and Connectives

Make all necessary corrections in the use of adjectives, adverbs, prepositions, and conjunctions in the manner indicated in the example.

EXAMPLE: _____*That*_____ _____*other*_____ ~~That there~~ house looks better than any ^ house in town. (674, 298)

_____ _____ 1 I don't know if he will come, but I sure hope he does. (381, 311)

_____ _____ 2 The smallest of the two boys skates very good. (296, 329)

_____ _____ 3 I read where the workers can easy finish the pool by June. (380, 339)

_____ _____ 4 The oldest of my two cousins is not as tall as you. (296, 310)

_____ _____ 5 Behave like you were taught or you won't have no friends. (372, 336)

_____ _____ 6 These kind of skate is some better than mine. (302, 334)

_____ _____ 7 We shall be accompanied with three other boys beside my brother. (355, 353)

_____ _____ 8 Ed was kind of angry at Jo for taking the car. (333, 351)

_____ _____ 9 If they will agree with our plan, we will sure have a good time. (350, 311)

_____ _____ 10 No less than ten people can play that kind of a game. (306, 307)

_____ _____ 11 Nowheres can you find a steak more tastier than this. (330, 295)

_____ _____ 12 Our senior team played good, and the other team played sort of badly. (329, 333)

_____ _____ 13 Jane is taller than anyone in her class, but she is not as tall as her teacher. (298, 310)

_____ _____ 14 Kay swims good, and her strokes look beautifully. (329, 289)

_____ _____ 15 Most all of us feel some better after a trip. (328, 334)

_____ _____ 16 There wasn't no one who finished inside an hour. (336, 356)

_____ _____ 17 He told us to omit the six last pages like we expected. (303, 372)

_____ _____ 18 Bob only caught four bass and a eel while fishing. (340, 286)

_____ _____ 19 If he had behaved different, he would not feel badly now. (311, 289)

_____ _____ 20 Sue did not feel as she could part from the money required for a new dress. (379, 362)

_____ _____ 21 This car is different than the old one, but I don't like this kind of a car. (361, 307)

_____ _____ 22 Neither Jim or Mary differs from me in political beliefs. (378, 360)

_____ _____ 23 The vase fell off of the table and rolled in back of the door. (364, 363)

_____ _____ 24 This kind of program are different than the ones we watched last year. (302, 361)

_____ _____ 25 Helen divided the candy among the twins like Mother told her. (354, 372)

V. Sentence Effectiveness

Each item consists of two expressions of the same thought. On the line before the number of the sentence, write **A** or **B** to indicate which is the better sentence.

EXAMPLE: <u>A</u> **A** Jim likes to play games, especially tennis and baseball.
    B Jim likes to play games. Especially tennis and baseball.

___1 **A** Driving through the deep snow, many stalled cars were seen.
    B Driving through the deep snow, we saw many stalled cars.

___2 **A** Suzanne saw a bike in a shop which she liked very much.
    B In a shop Suzanne saw a bike which she liked very much.

___3 **A** Larry told Bob that he had been made the new goalkeeper.
    B Larry told Bob, "You have been made the new goalkeeper."

___4 **A** Hank and Charles had a good time while they were in Canada.
    B Hank and Charles had a good time. While they were in Canada.

___5 **A** Jack Norton is an excellent athlete, and he works on a farm in the summer.
    B Jack Norton, who is an excellent athlete, works on a farm in the summer.

Plain English Handbook, 433, 436, 438, 446, 447, 451, 452.

VI. Capitalization and Punctuation

Indicate the punctuation and capitalization needed at each point marked by a number in parentheses. Indicate a semicolon rather than a period wherever possible. Use the following key:

a — capital letter	**c** — comma	**e** — semicolon	**g** — question mark
b — small letter	**d** — period	**f** — quotation marks	**h** — hyphen

EXAMPLE: 1 _c_ 2 _c_ 3 _a_ 4 _a_ 5 _d_ Ed[1] Faye[2] and Al go to East [3]high [4]school[5] (504, 471, 486)

1___2___3___4___5___ 1 On [1]friday, [2]july 23[3] 1972[4] we left for the [5]canadian wilds. (469, 502, 468)

1___2___3___4___5___ 2 Al is[1] I believe[2] a hard[3]working[4] clever senior[5] he deserves the award. (500, 532, 505, 490)

1___2___3___4___5___ 3 Did you hear Bill say[1] [2][3]we must win this game[4][5] (501, 507, 466, 514, 529)

1___2___3___4___5___ 4 Last [1]Summer we visited [2]memphis[3] [4]tennessee[5] (470, 468, 500, 486)

1___2___3___4___5___ 5 My [1]Mother said, [2][3]if you want to go[4] you should pack now.[5] (482, 507, 466, 497)

1___2___3___4___5___ 6 [1]that farmer raises corn[2] rye[3] oats[4] and barley[5] however, wheat is his principal crop. (464, 504, 490)

1___2___3___4___5___ 7 Margaret Mitchell[1] who wrote [2]*gone with the* [3]*wind*[4] lived in the [5]south. (499, 478, 474)

1___2___3___4___5___ 8 Twenty[1]six students from [2]wade [3]high [4]school are trying for the scholarship[5] (534, 471, 486)

1___2___3___4___5___ 9 Mr. Black lives [1]North of [2]kansas [3]city[4] however, he works in St[5] Joseph. (474, 468, 490, 487)

SCORE _____ (Top Score 200)

Final Inventory/B

I. *Sentence Sense* 10 Points

On the line preceding each group of words, write **0** if the group is not a complete sentence; write **1** if the group is one complete sentence; or write **2** if the group is two sentences incorrectly written as one.

EXAMPLE: _0_ When the dentist had finished.

___ 1 I am going to the circus tomorrow, I am going with Jim.

___ 2 By working hard, Bill has accomplished much.

___ 3 Running to catch the bounding ball.

___ 4 Expecting to become a noted author, Alice writes many stories.

___ 5 After Fred had finished his work and had gone home.

___ 6 Spent last summer in the mountains of New Hampshire.

___ 7 Hal is captain of the hockey team all his teammates like him.

___ 8 When did Juanita say that she would arrive?

___ 9 Unless he does better work in English.

___10 Because the day was hot and humid.

Plain English Handbook, 1–4, 33–37.

II. *Classifying Sentences and Parts of Speech* 30 Points

On the first line preceding each sentence, indicate its class by writing **S** for simple, **Cd** for compound, or **Cx** for complex. On the next two lines, indicate the part of speech of each of the two italicized words by writing **n** for noun, **pron** for pronoun, **adj** for adjective, **adv** for adverb, **v** for verb, **prep** for preposition, or **conj** for conjunction. Class the conjunctive adverb as a conjunction.

EXAMPLE: _S_ _n_ _adv_ *Terry* and he go sailing *nearly* every day.

___ ___ ___ 1 Miss Lind *liked* our program, particularly the *musical* numbers.

___ ___ ___ 2 The pumpkin pie looked *good*, but we did *not* taste it.

___ ___ ___ 3 Hank Wilson is *friendly; however,* somehow he is not very popular.

___ ___ ___ 4 Ellen *and* the others have gone *to* the show.

___ ___ ___ 5 There are *only* ten people in our club *now*.

___ ___ ___ 6 Mary thinks that *"but"* is always a *conjunction*.

___ ___ ___ 7 *This* is the best book *I* have ever read.

___ ___ ___ 8 We drove very slowly after *we* reached the *school* grounds.

___ ___ ___ 9 I must give *this* table a smooth finish *before* I leave.

___ ___ ___10 If we *work* hard, we can finish this job *before* noon.

Plain English Handbook, 20–23, 38–45, 52, 138–140, 320.

Correct each incorrect noun, pronoun, or verb by writing the correct forms on the lines preceding the sentence.

EXAMPLE: _____*she*_____ _____*were*_____ _____*came*_____ Dick and ~~her was~~ there when I ~~come.~~ (149, 247, 204, 216)

_____ _____ _____ 1 Bob could of helped she and I if he had been on time. (230, 153)

_____ _____ _____ 2 Joy, one of those people who is always active, and Pam each brung their racket. (241, 204, 163)

_____ _____ _____ 3 Twenty dollars were gave to the chairperson to help we members finance the next dance. (245, 204, 157)

_____ _____ _____ 4 Was Dick and him here when the coach give the new instructions? (247, 149, 204, 216)

_____ _____ _____ 5 The childrens' shrill crys attracted a police officers attention. (122, 80, 120)

_____ _____ _____ 6 Neither Frank nor she think that you was later than her. (237, 260, 148)

_____ _____ _____ 7 A number of employees was setting on the steps while I laid on the grass. (244, 204, 217)

_____ _____ _____ 8 Don't Betty speak as if she was angry with Tom and he? (197, 258, 153)

_____ _____ _____ 9 It was him and her whom we believed would arrange the program. (152, 159)

_____ _____ _____ 10 Ted and me saw Jim and she while they were picking blueberrys. (149, 153, 80)

_____ _____ _____ 11 Us three ate ham and eggs, which are a good food, and drunk lemonade. (151, 247, 204)

_____ _____ _____ 12 There comes Bob and him to help we players with our forward passes. (239, 149, 157)

_____ _____ _____ 13 Jan and Lou's new long skirts were tore by Toms dog. (125, 204, 120)

_____ _____ _____ 14 Whom do you think had ought to help we actors with the next play? (159, 225, 157)

_____ _____ _____ 15 To get its uniforms, the band has to go to whoever the director selects. (165, 240, 162)

_____ _____ _____ 16 If I was there, I could help Pat and he learn Jan to swim. (256, 153, 227)

_____ _____ _____ 17 Each member of the class except he and I want to go to the race. (153, 242)

_____ _____ _____ 18 Neither the boys nor I were surprised by Al winning the bucketsful of pennies at the fair. (238, 270, 87)

_____ _____ _____ 19 The Browns have ponys, sheeps, cows, and many calfs on their farm. (80, 89, 82)

_____ _____ _____ 20 Us organizers should invite the two boy's brother-in-laws to the picnic. (151, 121, 86)

IV. Modifiers and Connectives

Make all necessary corrections in the use of adjectives, adverbs, prepositions, and conjunctions in the manner indicated in the example.

EXAMPLE: _____saw only_____ _____from_____ I only saw one player with a bat different than mine. (340, 361)

_____ _____ 1 Not none of us would do the job different. (336, 311)

_____ _____ 2 I agree with Joanne's plan that we divide the work among the two of them. (350, 354)

_____ _____ 3 Among the two artists, the work will be completed easy. (354, 339)

_____ _____ 4 There wasn't no reason for Ed's only working an hour. (336, 340)

_____ _____ 5 The tallest of the two ladders stands in back of the barn. (296, 363)

_____ _____ 6 We should arrive at Toronto by noon easy. (352, 339)

_____ _____ 7 I saw in the local paper where Jo was accompanied with her mother on the trip. (380, 355)

_____ _____ 8 The flowers smell sweetly, and they are real lovely. (289, 311)

_____ _____ 9 Glenn feels badly about failing, but he hasn't no one to blame but himself. (289, 336)

_____ _____ 10 The boy dived off of the dock in the lake. (364, 357)

_____ _____ 11 She wouldn't divide the candy between the three children except they were quiet. (354, 370)

_____ _____ 12 Jan does her work prompt, and she does it good. (311, 329)

_____ _____ 13 Dad feels some better, but he can go nowheres for a week. (334, 330)

_____ _____ 14 If you drive careful, the box should not fall off of the truck. (311, 364)

_____ _____ 15 Most all teenagers like these kind of movie. (328, 302)

_____ _____ 16 Joan differs from you about cars, and she believes this one is the best of the two. (360, 296)

_____ _____ 17 He is sort of angry at us for leaving. (333, 351)

_____ _____ 18 I do not know if he will come, but I hope he does arrive inside of an hour. (381, 356)

_____ _____ 19 We omitted the ten last pages like she said. (303, 372)

_____ _____ 20 Bill is not as old as Jim, but he is sure more mature. (310, 311)

_____ _____ 21 Less than six members like that kind of a play. (306, 307)

_____ _____ 22 Neither Dot or Hal dances good enough yet. (378, 329)

_____ _____ 23 The lecturer spoke clear and distinct. (311)

_____ _____ 24 I don't feel as I can agree with your plan. (379, 350)

_____ _____ 25 Most all of us are singing kind of better now. (328, 333)

V. *Sentence Effectiveness*   5 Points

Each item consists of two expressions of the same thought. On the line before the number of the sentence, write **A** or **B** to indicate which is the better sentence.

EXAMPLE: <u>B</u> **A** Hank did some chores. Before he came to school today.
                   B Hank did some chores before he came to school today.

___1 **A** Playing games and singing songs, we enjoyed the evening.
    B Playing games and singing songs, the evening was enjoyed.

___2 **A** Nonita likes fruit. Particularly cherries.
    B Nonita likes fruit, particularly cherries.

___3 **A** Margaret told Louisa that she had been invited to the wedding.
    B Margaret said, "Louisa, I've been invited to the wedding."

___4 **A** Mary Matthews, the president of our class, has an aunt living in Paris.
    B Mary Matthews is the president of our class she has an aunt living in Paris.

___5 **A** Todd saw a picture in the exhibit which he thought was very odd.
    B In the exhibit Todd saw a picture which he thought was very odd.

Plain English Handbook, 433, 436, 438, 439, 445, 446, 451, 452.

VI. *Capitalization and Punctuation*   45 Points

Indicate the punctuation and capitalization needed at each point marked by a number in parentheses. Indicate a semicolon rather than a period wherever possible. Use the following key:

a — capital letter   c — comma   e — semicolon   g — question mark
b — small letter   d — period   f — quotation marks   h — hyphen

EXAMPLE: 1 _c_ 2 _c_ 3 _b_ 4 _c_ 5 _d_   No(1) Mary(2) my (3)Cousin(4) is from the (5)north.   (498, 500, 482, 474)

1 __ 2 __ 3 __ 4 __ 5 __ 1 Before I came to Sims (1)high (2)school(3) I went to a school (4)North of St(5) Louis. (471, 497, 474, 487)

1 __ 2 __ 3 __ 4 __ 5 __ 2 Jane is(1) I believe(2) a capable(3) hard(4) working student(5) she deserves success. (500, 505, 532, 489)

1 __ 2 __ 3 __ 4 __ 5 __ 3 Next (1)monday my (2)Mother and (3)i will visit Ruth Harris(4) my oldest (5)Cousin. (469, 482, 479, 500)

1 __ 2 __ 3 __ 4 __ 5 __ 4 She asked, "(1)what can you tell us about the present (2)united (3)states (4)congress?(5) (466, 468, 471, 507)

1 __ 2 __ 3 __ 4 __ 5 __ 5 When you were in the (1)south last (2)Spring(3) did you visit (4)atlanta(5) (474, 470, 497, 468, 529)

1 __ 2 __ 3 __ 4 __ 5 __ 6 Twenty(1)six (2)Seniors have enrolled for (3)french(4) history(5) and English. (534, 471, 468, 504)

1 __ 2 __ 3 __ 4 __ 5 __ 7 (1)did Bill say(2) (3)I'll be here early(4) (5) (464, 501, 507, 514)

1 __ 2 __ 3 __ 4 __ 5 __ 8 No(1) our (2)History class isn't studying the (3)spanish-(4)american (5)war. (498, 471) 468)

1 __ 2 __ 3 __ 4 __ 5 __ 9 Harry went to our (1)High (2)School(3) however he lives in Ames(4) Iowa(5) now. (471, 490, 500)

SCORE _____ (Top Score 200)

Final Inventory/C

I. *Sentence Sense*   10 Points

On the line before each group of words, write **0** if the group is not a complete sentence; write **1** if the group is one complete sentence; write **2** if the group is two sentences incorrectly written as one; or write **3** if the group is three sentences incorrectly written as one.

EXAMPLE: __0__ Before the final plans had been completed.

___ 1 Went to the organ recital with Johnnie last night.

___ 2 After they have made the plans, they will report to the club.

___ 3 That green house across the street is the one I like.

___ 4 Have been waiting to see the new track coach.

___ 5 Read Jane's latest letter when you have time.

___ 6 Our club is planning a carnival everyone is to take part you must plan to go.

___ 7 Hoping to win the state title, the team played its best.

___ 8 Cindy is the president, she will appoint a new by-laws committee.

___ 9 At the time when everyone was busy.

___10 Expecting to go to the Canadian Rockies.

Plain English Handbook, 1–4, 33–37.

II. *Essential Parts of the Sentence*   10 Points

On the first line before each sentence, write the simple subject. On the second line, write the simple predicate.

EXAMPLE: ____*work*____ _____*Can be completed*_____ Can the work be completed soon?

_____ _____1 Hearing a siren, we looked for a police car.

_____ _____2 Having eaten lunch, Ben went to play tennis.

_____ _____3 Have they forgotten about the meeting?

_____ _____4 Could John have been told that I won?

_____ _____5 From the hills came the sound of thunder.

Plain English Handbook, 3, 4, 13, 15.

III. *Classifying Sentences and Sentence Parts*   30 Points

On the first line classify the sentence as to form by writing **S** for simple, **Cd** for compound, **Cx** for complex, or **Cd-Cx** for compound-complex. On the second line indicate whether the italicized group of words is a phrase or a clause by writing **P** or **C**. On the third line indicate the use of the phrase or clause by writing **n** for noun, **adj** for adjective, or **adv** for adverb.

EXAMPLE: ___*Cd*_ _*P*_ _*adv*___ *In the garden* grew scarlet roses, and the air was fragrant.

_____ __ _____ 1 That boy *running down the street* stole the money.

_____ __ _____ 2 The truth is *that she did her best.*

_____ __ _____ 3 The woman *seated on the platform* is our administrative principal.

_____ — _____ 4 Quickly we accepted the offer *that he made.*

_____ — _____ 5 We began the work, but we didn't finish *until you came.*

_____ — _____ 6 Helen and I walked *around the block.*

_____ — _____ 7 He told stories *of pioneer days,* and we listened.

_____ — _____ 8 *To accomplish a great task* requires much effort.

_____ — _____ 9 The plane had left *before we reached the airport.*

_____ — _____ 10 Great deeds are accomplished by those *who have ambition.*

Plain English Handbook, 389–416.

IV. *Defective Sentences*   5 Points

Each item consists of two expressions of the same thought. On the line before each number, write **A** or **B** to indicate which is the better sentence.

EXAMPLE: <u>A</u> **A** Ms. Hernandez, a mathematics teacher, plays the organ.
                   B Ms. Hernandez is a mathematics teacher, and she plays the organ.

___1 **A** Walking swiftly, we soon reached our destination.
      B Walking swiftly, our destination was soon reached.

___2 **A** As we drove through the park, we almost saw fifty buffaloes.
      B As we drove through the park, we saw almost fifty buffaloes.

___3 **A** Nell told Jean that she had won the prize.
      B Nell said, "Jean, you have won the prize."

___4 **A** Robert is intelligent and has ambition.
      B Robert is intelligent and ambitious.

___5 **A** He held a spear in his hand that was made of wood.
      B In his hand he held a spear that was made of wood.

Plain English Handbook, 340, 433, 439, 450, 451, 452.

V. *Capitalization and Punctuation in the Sentence*   45 Points

Indicate the changes needed in these sentences by writing the appropriate letter from the following key beside each number at the left.

a — capital letter	d — period	g — question mark	j — dash
b — small letter	e — semicolon	h — quotation marks	k — no change
c — comma	f — hyphen	i — colon	

EXAMPLE: 1 <u>b</u> 2 <u>b</u> 3 <u>a</u> 4 <u>c</u> 5 <u>d</u> Last [1]Summer my [2]Mother went to [3]onawa[4] [5]iowa. (470, 482, 468, 500)

1___ 2___ 3___ 4___ 5___ 1 The [1]Juniors very much like the following subjects[2] [3]History, [4]french, and [5]english. (471, 493)

1___ 2___ 3___ 4___ 5___ 2 Pam was on television on Thursday[1] [2]march 20[3] [4]did you see her[5] (502, 469, 445, 486, 464, 529)

1___ 2___ 3___ 4___ 5___ 3 Who said[1] [2]The [3]Fall season is the best of all[4] [5] (501, 507, 470, 514)

1___ 2___ 3___ 4___ 5___ 4 Jane asked, [1]Where were you during [2]christmas[3] Susan[4] [5] (507, 469, 500, 529, 514)

1___ 2___ 3___ 4___ 5___ 5 Mrs[1] Orr[2] the [3]Superintendent of our schools, lived in the [4]east[5] however, she likes the West. (487, 500, 481, 474, 490)

1___ 2___ 3___ 4___ 5___ 6 The trees in [1]oberon [2]park are gorgeous[3] especially the oaks[4] elms[5] and maples. (468, 484, 499, 504)

1___ 2___ 3___ 4___ 5___ 7 Esther[1] did you see [2]miss Coleman[3] your [4]Mathematics teacher[5] (500, 481, 471, 529)

¹__²__³__⁴__⁵__ 8 If you will check¹ you will find that there are fifty²six pages in ³*exploring* ⁴*the* ⁵*sun*. (497, 534, 478)

¹__²__³__⁴__⁵__ 9 We drove twenty¹three miles ²north, and there they were³ Bob⁴ Ernie⁵ and Sandy. (534, 474, 523, 504)

VI. *Using Substantives and Verbs in the Sentence*   40 Points

On the lines at the left, write the numbers of the bold-faced words that make each sentence correct.

EXAMPLE: _2_ _2_ ¹**Has**/²**Have** Bob and Don ¹**did**/²**done** their work yet? (247, 204, 216)

__ __ 1 Yesterday I ¹**give**/²**gave** the monkeys several ¹**handsful**/²**handfuls** of peanuts. (193, 204, 216, 87)

__ __ 2 There ¹**was**/²**were** two squirrels ¹**sitting**/²**setting** on the wall. (239, 204, 217)

__ __ 3 ¹**Doesn't**/²**Don't** he know that the stolen car was ¹**yours**/²**your's**? (197, 146)

__ __ 4 Each of the men ¹**were**/²**was** in ¹**his**/²**their** place on time. (242, 163)

__ __ 5 Bob and I ¹**seen**/²**saw** several ¹**deer**/²**deers** last summer. (193, 204, 216, 89)

__ __ 6 ¹**We**/²**Us** sophomores could have ¹**went**/²**gone** with Joan and him. (151, 204, 216)

__ __ 7 King was ¹**lying**/²**laying** there while ¹**we**/²**us** three looked for him. (204, 217, 151)

__ __ 8 ¹**Weren't**/²**Wasn't** you here when we read about ¹**Ed**/²**Ed's** winning the car? (260, 127)

__ __ 9 Jo and ¹**her**/²**she** have ¹**given**/²**gave** it to me who am the leader. (149, 204, 216)

__ __10 Neither the boys nor Ann ¹**is**/²**are** to go with ¹**we**/²**us** girls. (238, 157)

__ __11 Both of her ¹**sister-in-laws**/²**sisters-in-law** receive high ¹**salarys**/²**salaries**. (86, 80)

__ __12 If I ¹**was**/²**were** you, I would ¹**accept**/²**except** the offer. (256, 228)

__ __13 Are you sure it was they ¹**whom**/²**who** we ¹**saw**/²**seen** today? (160, 204, 216)

__ __14 ¹**Whomever**/²**Whoever** we invite will please Jo and ¹**she**/²**her**. (162, 153)

__ __15 ¹**Is**/²**Are** Jan and her sister making all the ¹**actors'**/²**actors** costumes? (247, 121)

__ __16 I wish I ¹**were**/²**was** going to Paris with Jean and ¹**she**/²**her**. (256, 153)

__ __17 The ¹**childrens'**/²**children's** toys were ¹**broke**/²**broken** when we found them. (122, 185, 204)

__ __18 Bob and ¹**him**/²**he** should ¹**of**/²**have** shown it to us tutors. (149, 230)

__ __19 Either the twins or Dad ¹**are**/²**is** going to meet ¹**us**/²**we** travelers. (238, 157)

__ __20 He gave new ¹**pianos**/²**pianoes** to his ¹**daughters-in-law**/²**daughter-in-laws**. (78, 86)

VII. *Using Modifiers and Connectives in the Sentence*   20 Points

On the lines at the left, write the numbers of the bold-faced words that make each sentence correct.

EXAMPLE: _2_ _2_ I read ¹**where**/²**that** ¹**those**/²**that** kind of scissors is on sale now. (380, 302)

__ __ 1 ¹**Almost**/²**Most** all the participants played ¹**like**/²**as if** they were tired. (328, 372)

__ __ 2 Dan was ¹**kind of**/²**rather** frightened when he ran ¹**into**/²**in** the house. (333, 357)

__ __ 3 The six boys were angry ¹at/²with Al, for he didn't divide the money ¹between/²among them. (351, 354)

__ __ 4 It seems ¹like/²that he can't ¹never/²ever dive the right way. (372, 336)

__ __ 5 The players ¹surely/²sure do feel ¹bad/²badly about defaulting the game. (311, 312)

__ __ 6 Neither Ed ¹or/²nor Alicia sing well, but Ed sings the ¹better/²best. (378, 296)

__ __ 7 Sue finished her work ¹easily/²easy, but did not do it so ¹good/²well as Paul. (339, 329)

__ __ 8 His story ¹surely/²sure is different ¹from/²than the one that Ed told. (311, 337)

__ __ 9 We looked ¹behind/²in back of the sofa, but we didn't see ¹any/²no keys. (363, 336)

__ __10 The ¹oldest/²older of the two brothers won't work unless you pay him ¹well/²good. (296, 329)

VIII. *Using Words in the Sentence*   40 Points

On the lines at the left write the numbers of the bold-faced words that make each sentence correct.

EXAMPLE: _2_ _1_ ¹Was/²Were you there when he ¹gave/²give the assignment? (260, 204, 216)

__ __ 1 I am sure that Liz will ¹teach/²learn Tom and ¹him/²he to swim. (227, 272)

__ __ 2 Jane ¹doesn't/²don't feel at all ¹bad/²badly about it. (197, 289, 312)

__ __ 3 That kind ¹of a/²of wide-brimmed hat looks ¹well/²good on Marie. (307, 289, 312)

__ __ 4 I read in the paper ¹where/²that they haven't found ¹no/²any clues. (380, 336)

__ __ 5 Sam may fail in math ¹except/²unless you and ¹I/²me help him. (370, 149)

__ __ 6 ¹Hull/²Hull's and Smith's store has ten ¹basketfuls/²basketsful of plums. (124, 87)

__ __ 7 ¹Was/²Were Grace and Jean ¹setting/²sitting in Row C? (247, 204, 217)

__ __ 8 ¹Them/²Those campers won't listen to ¹us/²we leaders. (168, 157)

__ __ 9 Why can't she act ¹as/²like my two ¹sister-in-laws/²sisters-in-law do? (372, 86)

__ __10 Neither Ruth ¹or/²nor Tina mentioned it to ¹us/²we reporters. (378, 157)

__ __11 Every one of the men ¹were/²was in ¹his/²their own seat. (242, 163)

__ __12 If I ¹was/²were she, I would ¹lie/²lay in the hammock. (256, 204, 217)

__ __13 The ¹men's/²mens' ¹wifes/²wives are also doctors. (122, 82)

__ __14 ¹Wasn't/²Weren't your books ¹lying/²laying on that table? (197, 204, 217)

__ __15 He saw Mary and ¹me/²I when we ran from the car ¹into/²in the house. (153, 357)

__ __16 Was it ¹she/²her whom you ¹seen/²saw? (152, 204, 216)

__ __17 Each of the boys did ¹their/²his part very ¹well/²good indeed. (163, 329)

__ __18 ¹Whomever/²Whoever you choose ¹should/²had ought to start working. (162, 225)

__ __19 He is one of ¹them/²those persons who ¹are/²is naturally polite. (168, 241)

__ __20 ¹These/²This kind of sheep ¹has/²have more wool. (302, 197)

124

SCORE _____ (Top Score 200)

Final Inventory/D

I. *Sentence Sense*   10 Points

On the line before each group of words, write **o** if the group is not a complete sentence; write **1** if the group is one complete sentence; write **2** if the group is two sentences incorrectly written as one; or write **3** if the group is three sentences incorrectly written as one.

EXAMPLE: <u>o</u> On the table where I laid it.

__ 1 The man over there on the corner is the one I asked.

__ 2 Wrote a letter to Laurie in Scotland today.

__ 3 Report to the director of physical training as soon as you finish.

__ 4 It was an excellent radio program, did you hear it?

__ 5 Wishing to see all the games, we bought season tickets.

__ 6 As I was driving along the highway in my new sports car.

__ 7 It will be a good game our team is sure to win you should be there.

__ 8 Writing stories for one of the leading magazines.

__ 9 Before we announce the class day plans, we must have the principal's approval.

__10 After the plans for the party have been completed.

Plain English Handbook, 1–4, 33–37.

II. *Essential Parts of the Sentence*   10 Points

On the first line before each sentence, write the simple subject. On the second line, write the simple predicate.

EXAMPLE: <u>watch</u>   <u>Can be repaired</u>   Can this watch be easily repaired?

_____ _____1 Down the street came Mark carrying a flag.

_____ _____2 From the field came the loud report of a gun.

_____ _____3 Did your friend remember to bring the pickles?

_____ _____4 Neither of them seemed sad to be going.

_____ _____5 There was a row of trees beside the road.

Plain English Handbook, 3, 4, 13, 15.

III. *Classifying Sentences and Sentence Parts*   30 Points

On the first line classify the sentence as to form by writing **S** for simple, **Cd** for compound, **Cx** for complex, or **Cd-Cx** for compound-complex. On the second line indicate whether the italicized group of words is a phrase or a clause by writing **P** or **C**. On the third line indicate the use of the phrase or clause by writing **n** for noun, **adj** for adjective, or **adv** for adverb.

EXAMPLE: <u>Cd-Cx</u> <u>C</u> <u>n</u> The child accepted the money *that was offered him.*

_____ __ _____ 1 That man *painting the picture* is a famous artist.

_____ __ _____ 2 We saw Tom *as soon as he walked into the room.*

_____ __ _____ 3 Is this the picture *that Dorothy painted?*

_____ __ _____ 4 Janet's ambition is *to become a doctor.*

_____ __ _____ 5 His ideas are good, but he wishes *that he could speak well.*

_____ __ _____ 6 Lucile promised *that she would work for us.*

_____ __ _____ 7 *When the time comes,* Louisa will do her part.

_____ __ _____ 8 Don left *after the bell rang.*

_____ __ _____ 9 Both teams played well, but our team won *by a large score.*

_____ __ _____ 10 He tried his best, and he was praised *by all his friends.*

Plain English Handbook, 389–416.

IV. *Defective Sentences*   5 Points

Each item consists of two expressions of the same thought. On the line before each number write **A** or **B** to indicate which is the better sentence.

EXAMPLE: <u>A</u>   **A** Wandering through the shadowy woods, we enjoyed the day.
          B Wandering through the shadowy woods, the day was enjoyed.

__1 **A** To do one's duty is better than shirking one's responsibility.
    B To do one's duty is better than to shirk one's responsibility.

__2 **A** Jill is our class president, and she likes chess.
    B Jill, our class president, likes chess.

__3 **A** We drove nearly six hundred miles the second day.
    B We nearly drove six hundred miles the second day.

__4 **A** You gave an apple to the child that was green.
    B You gave the child an apple that was green.

__5 **A** Tom told George that he had been chosen captain.
    B Tom said, "George, you have been chosen captain."

Plain English Handbook, 433, 436, 439, 450–452.

V. *Capitalization and Punctuation in the Sentence*   45 Points

Indicate the changes needed in these sentences by writing the appropriate letter from the following key beside each number at the left.

a — capital letter   d — period   g — question mark   j — dash
b — small letter   e — semicolon   h — quotation marks   k — no change
c — comma   f — hyphen   i — colon

EXAMPLE: ¹<u>d</u> ²<u>c</u> ³<u>a</u> ⁴<u>d</u> ⁵<u>a</u>   Dan's party will be on ¹friday² ³april 15⁴ ⁵will you attend it?   (469, 502, 486, 444, 464)

¹__²__³__⁴__⁵__ 1 In the ¹summer the flowers are pretty² ³especially the roses⁴ daisies⁵ and petunias. (470, 499, 446, 504)

¹__²__³__⁴__⁵__ 2 I go to Wilson ¹High ²School³ ⁴where do you attend school⁵ (471, 445, 486, 464, 529)

¹__²__³__⁴__⁵__ 3 Who said¹ ² ³democracy must begin at home⁴ ⁵   (501, 507, 466, 514)

¹__²__³__⁴__⁵__ 4 Bob¹ Mrs² Flint, the ³principal of our school, comes from the ⁴west⁵ nevertheless, she is happy here. (500, 487, 481, 474, 490)

¹__²__³__⁴__⁵__ 5 Dick¹ when you visited your ²aunt on ³labor ⁴day⁵ did you meet Olga Williams?   (500, 482, 469, 497)

¹__²__³__⁴__⁵__ 6 Did Miss Rand¹ your ²English teacher³ ever live in Dickens⁴ Texas⁵ (500, 471, 529)

¹__²__³__⁴__⁵__ 7 Many ¹Seniors are taking the following subjects² ³spanish, ⁴Sociology, and ⁵history. (471, 493)

¹__²__³__⁴__⁵__ 8 "Did you know there were twenty ¹ four people in our group when we visited ²Carlsbad ³caverns⁴ ⁵ asked Fred. (534, 473, 484, 514, 507)

¹__²__³__⁴__⁵__ 9 The cover of our school magazine, ¹tiger Times² is decorated in our school colors³ blue⁴ white⁵ and gold. (478, 500, 523, 504)

VI. Using Substantives and Verbs in the Sentence

On the lines at the left, write the numbers of the bold-faced words or phrases that make each sentence correct.

EXAMPLE: _1_ _1_ Those ¹knives/²knifes must have been ¹broken/²broke when we bought them.   (82, 204)

— — 1 The pen was ¹laying/²lying there while ¹us/²we four were looking for it.   (204, 217, 151)

— — 2 ¹Don't/²Doesn't Ricardo want to go with ¹we/²us hikers?   (197, 157)

— — 3 There ¹were/²was three empty seats when Betty and I ¹came/²come in.   (239, 204, 216)

— — 4 Here ¹comes/²come Joe and ¹him/²he with the popcorn for us.   (247, 149)

— — 5 Is it ¹me/²I who am to direct the ¹boy's and girl's/²boys' and girls' games at an informal get-to-gether?   (152, 121)

— — 6 ¹Was/²Were the monkeys lying in their cage when you and Steve ¹saw/²seen them?   (197, 204, 216)

— — 7 Paul and he were sure that the ¹ponys/²ponies were ¹ours/²our's.   (80, 146)

— — 8 Fred and she ¹did/²done most of the ¹painters/²painters' work.   (204, 416, 121)

— — 9 My mother ¹gave/²give Len and me four ¹cupsful/²cupfuls of sugar for fudge.   (204, 416, 87)

— —10 I am sure you ¹was/²were there when Julie told us about ¹Tom's/²Tom offering to sell tickets.   (260, 127)

— —11 I am sure it was ¹her/²she ¹whom/²who we saw at the poster exhibit.   (152, 160)

— —12 Either the scouts or their leader ¹is/²are responsible for repairing the ¹childrens'/²children's toys.   (238, 122)

— —13 ¹Have/²Has Connie and Ben ¹shown/²showed you the color photos of us?   (247, 204)

— —14 If I ¹was/²were she, I would ¹except/²accept the offer Roberto made.   (256, 228)

— —15 We will bring ¹whoever/²whomever will help you and ¹him/²he.   (161, 153)

— —16 Every one of the women ¹was/²were in ¹their/²her place ten minutes before the board meeting began.   (246, 164)

— —17 Neither Anna nor Jim ¹plans/²plan to do what ¹we/²us officers suggested.   (238, 151)

— —18 I wish Ann ¹was/²were going with ¹us/²we skiers.   (256, 157)

— —19 Both of his ¹son-in-laws/²sons-in-law sell and repair ¹radioes/²radios.   (86, 79)

— —20 ¹Us/²We photographers could ¹have/²of gone with Dick and him if we had only known it.   (151, 230)

VII. Using Modifiers and Connectives in the Sentence

On the lines at the left, write the numbers of the bold-faced words that make each sentence correct.

EXAMPLE: _2_ _1_ The ¹most/²more bashful of the twins won't sing ¹unless/²without you urge him.   (296, 370)

— — 1 This book ¹surely/²sure is different ¹than/²from the movie made from it.   (311, 361)

— — 2 It seems ¹like/²that he won't do ¹anything/²nothing to help us.   (372, 336)

___ ___ 3 I looked ¹behind/²in back of the house, but there wasn't ¹no/²any cat. (363, 336)

___ ___ 4 Kim and she ¹surely/²sure feel ¹bad/²badly about it. (311, 312)

___ ___ 5 Will ¹these/²this kind of shoe wear very ¹well/²good? (302, 329)

___ ___ 6 I read ¹that/²where the estate will be equally divided ¹between/²among the four heirs. (380, 354)

___ ___ 7 ¹Almost/²Most all the singers acted as if they were angry ¹at/²with us. (328, 351)

___ ___ 8 Neither Beth ¹or/²nor Mike can dance ¹very/²real well. (378, 311)

___ ___ 9 Bob looked ¹rather/²kind of tired when he walked ¹in/²into the room. (333, 357)

___ ___10 Neither Bill ¹nor/²or Janet skated very well, but I think Janet skated ¹better/²best. (378, 296)

VIII. *Using Words in the Sentence*

40 Points

On the lines at the left write the numbers of the bold-faced words that make each sentence correct.

EXAMPLE: _1_ _1_ ¹Are/²Is my hat and coat ¹lying/²laying on the bed? (247, 204, 217)

___ ___ 1 Neither Bob ¹or/²nor Don ¹should/²had ought to carry the trunk. (378, 225)

___ ___ 2 When we came ¹into/²in the house, we ¹seen/²saw Joan. (357, 204, 216)

___ ___ 3 ¹Doesn't/²Don't each of the youths want to bring ¹their/²his father? (197, 163)

___ ___ 4 ¹Us/²We girls were sure that the book was ¹your's/²yours. (151, 146)

___ ___ 5 Why can't he ¹set/²sit down ¹as/²like he should? (204, 217, 372)

___ ___ 6 ¹Them/²Those jars may fall ¹except/²unless you are careful. (168, 370)

___ ___ 7 The ¹smallest/²smaller of the two brothers ¹weren't/²wasn't there. (296, 246)

___ ___ 8 ¹Wasn't/²Weren't you here when the money was given to ¹we/²us treasurers? (260, 157)

___ ___ 9 His ¹son-in-laws/²sons-in-law were ¹setting/²sitting on the porch. (86, 204, 217)

___ ___10 The ¹workers'/²workers wet shoes were ¹lying/²laying on the floor. (121, 204, 217)

___ ___11 If I ¹was/²were he, I would bring ¹whomever/²whoever would come. (256, 161)

___ ___12 ¹Wasn't/²Weren't your parents in ¹Smith's/²Smith and Leon's store? (197, 124)

___ ___13 Does this kind ¹of a/²of poncho look ¹well/²good on me? (307, 329)

___ ___14 Jack feels ¹bad/²badly because he hasn't ¹no/²a ticket. (312, 336)

___ ___15 Neither of the sopranos did ¹their/²her part very ¹well/²good. (163, 329)

___ ___16 If I were ¹she/²her, I would ¹teach/²learn him to do it the right way. (152, 227)

___ ___17 It's one of the stories that ¹are/²is different ¹from/²than the others. (241, 337)

___ ___18 ¹Isn't/²Aren't ¹these/²this kind of tulip pretty? (197, 302)

___ ___19 ¹Thiefs/²Thieves stole several ¹womens'/²women's watches. (82, 122)

___ ___20 Did you read ¹where/²that Debbie and ¹she/²her had an accident? (380, 149)

128

SCORE _____ (Top Score 200)